COLORED ATLAS OF MINIATURE
CATFISH

EVERY SPECIES OF *CORYDORAS, BROCHIS & ASPIDORAS*

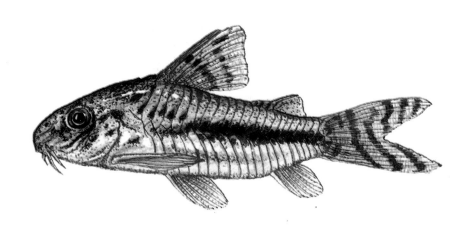

Corydoras bondi bondi.

DR. WARREN E. BURGESS
DRAWINGS BY JOHN R. QUINN

Anatomy of a *Corydoras* Catfish

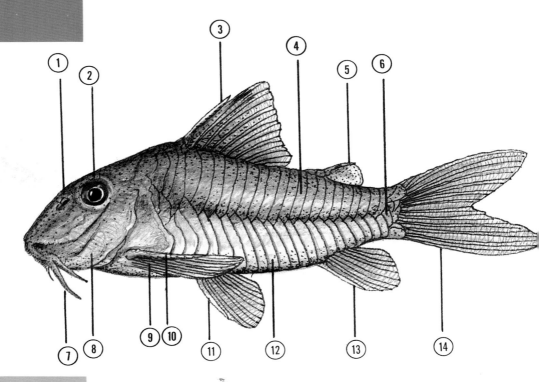

1. Nares; 2. Bony orbit of eye; 3. Dorsal spine; 4. Dorsolateral scutes; 5. Adipose fin; 6 Caudal peduncle; 7. Barbels; 8. Operculum; 9. Pectoral fin; 10. Pectoral spine; 11. Ventral fin; 12. Ventrolateral scutes; 13. Anal fin; 14. Caudal fin.

COLORED ATLAS OF MINIATURE
CATFISH

EVERY SPECIES OF *CORYDORAS, BROCHIS & ASPIDORAS*

DR. WARREN E. BURGESS

Corydoras barbatus. Photo by Dr. H. J. Franke.

Corydoras amapaensis.

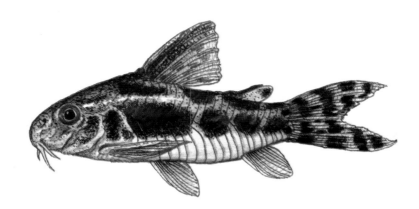

Distributed in the UNITED STATES by T.F.H. Publications, Inc., One T.F.H. Plaza, Neptune City, NJ 07753; in CANADA to the Pet Trade by H & L Pet Supplies Inc., 27 Kingston Crescent, Kitchener, Ontario N2B 2T6; Rolf C. Hagen Ltd., 3225 Sartelon Street, Montreal 382 Quebec; in CANADA to the Book Trade by Macmillan of Canada (A Division of Canada Publishing Corporation), 164 Commander Boulevard, Agincourt, Ontario M1S 3C7; in ENGLAND by T.F.H. Publications, PO Box 15, Waterlooville PO7 6BQ; in AUSTRALIA AND THE SOUTH PACIFIC by T.F.H. (Australia) Pty. Ltd., Box 149, Brookvale 2100 N.S.W., Australia; in NEW ZEALAND by Ross Haines & Son, Ltd., 82 D Elizabeth Knox Place, Panmure, Auckland, New Zealand; in the PHILIPPINES by Bio-Research, 5 Lippay Street, San Lorenzo Village, Makati, Rizal; in SOUTH AFRICA by Multipet Pty. Ltd., P.O. Box 35347, Northway, 4065, South Africa. Published by T.F.H. Publications, Inc. Manufactured in the United States of America by T.F.H. Publications, Inc.

CONTENTS

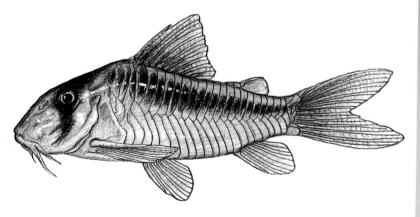

Corydoras micracanthus.

Corydoras burgessi. Photo by Dr. Warren E. Burgess.

CORYDORAS BROCHIS ASPIDORAS

Regardless of what other fishes might be housed in a community aquarium, there seem to be members of one particular genus that almost always are present. These are the corys, an aquaristically affectionate name for members of the genus *Corydoras*, a genus of catfishes that currently includes approximately 115 species. These small catfishes may have made their first appearance in aquaria in Europe as early as 1880, when it was reported that *Corydoras paleatus* was imported from Argentina, and they have maintained a place in the trade ever since. By about 1915 these fishes made their way to North America, where their popularity matched that accorded them by the Europeans.

Early aquarists kept corys mainly for their "scavenging" abilities as these catfishes (with few

Corydoras paleatus. Photo by Burkhard Kahl.

exceptions) are bottom feeders that scour the substrate for bits and pieces to eat. Anyone feeding their "regular" fishes did not have to be so circumspect as the corys were there to clean up after them. Most modern aquarists look at corys in a different light. They now treat them as interesting fishes in their own right and are as particular about their diet as they are of their other fishes, not relying as their forerunners did on leftover scraps that fell to the bottom and were missed or ignored by the more "important" tank residents.

The first introductions, most assuredly *Corydoras paleatus* and *C. aeneus*, were easy to keep and soon spawned. Even to this day these two species are the most prolific and most available of any of the cory species. Over the years, however, more *Corydoras* species were imported, many with very pleasing black spots or stripes and other markings, which seemed to be almost as cooperative as the first introductions. In recent years the popularity of corys has grown to such a level that new and different species are actively being sought in their native lands in order to help supply the growing demand. Even so, only about two dozen or so species are regularly imported and, of these, only a few of them are commercially raised. Corys in general are peaceful, comical, easy to maintain, relatively spawnable, active

Corydoras aeneus. Photo by Burkhard Kahl.

Aspidoras
pauciradiatus.
Photo by Alan
Pinkerton.

during the daytime, and have movable eyes that seem to follow their keeper about giving an occasional "wink" to let them know that all's well. Whether kept for their pleasing personalities as part of a community tank or as a species to be kept by themselves for breeding purposes, these fishes are solidly entrenched in the aquarium world and will undoubtedly remain there in the foreseeable future.

The genus *Corydoras* Lacepede, 1803, belongs to the armored catfish family Callichthyidae. Along with *Brochis* and *Aspidoras* they make up one of the two subfamilies of the family,

the Corydoradinae (the other subfamily is the Callichthyinae which includes, among others, the aquaristically familiar genera *Hoplosternum* and *Dianema*). *Corydoras*, *Brochis*, and *Aspidoras* are very similar, the differences being such that all the

Brochis splendens.

couple of these catfishes scurrying about the bottom busily searching for food.

Corys are distributed over South America from northern Argentina to Colombia. None grow very large, the average size being between 5 and 7 cm (2-3"), the largest, *C. barbatus,* about 12 cm (5"), the smallest (*C. hastatus, C. pygmaeus,* and *C. cochui*) a mere 2.5 cm (1"). The body is armored with two series of plates and the dorsal, pectoral, and adipose fins are each preceded by a "spine." Technically these are not true spines (although many an aquarist who has had a finger jabbed by one might want to argue the point) but hardened and modified soft rays. The armor not only helps prevent predation but if a cory happens to jump out of an aquarium it slows the drying out-process and may save its life if found quickly enough and returned to the tank.

species could easily be placed into a single genus. Many aquarists are familiar with species of these three genera as they all have representatives that are commonly imported for the aquarium trade. It is the largest genus, *Corydoras,* however, that provides the bulk of the hobby material. It is a rare sight, indeed, to see a community tank that does not have at least a

Most species of *Corydoras* are easy to care for and make no special demands on their keepers

Corydoras barbatus. Photo by H. J. Richter.

Corydoras pygmaeus. Photo by Burkhard Kahl.

temperatures (25°C or higher) include, among others, *C. schwartzi, C. bondi, C. trilineatus,* and *C. hastatus.* Spawning temperatures should be slightly higher than normal keeping temperatures, about 27° to 30°C, for most corys. Temporary drops to about 20°C are fairly well tolerated as well. Sudden changes in water chemistry and/or temperature can cause the corys to go into shock, actually "fainting" and falling over on their sides; most are quite hardy, however, and soon recover. However, slight, gradual changes in temperature (usually lower) are actually recommended as a means of precipitating spawning action in many corys as is massive water change (up to 90%). Normal aquarium lighting is appropriate for most corys as they are diurnal in nature, but the tank should also be provided with sheltered areas because of their shyness. Floating plants are an easy means to reduce the light level but still remain decorative. A well-planted tank is not only decorative

as far as water chemistry is concerned. Water of about neutral pH (6-8 is tolerated) and a hardness of about 5-15°dGH (2-25° is tolerated) is adequate. Proper temperatures depend upon where the species hails from as there are some relatively cool-water species that do not do well in tanks with high temperatures. Most corys, however, can usually survive within a temperature range of 12°C to 32°C (50°-90°F), though temperatures of 21° to 26°C are generally recommended for captive specimens. Those species that seem to prefer higher but also supplies (if broad-leaved plants are included) surfaces on which corys can deposit their eggs. Java fern is a particular favorite of both the fishes and the aquarists.

Feeding is also no problem as corys are omnivorous and almost any normal aquarium foods are acceptable, including frozen, freeze-dried, and even flake foods. Live foods are, of course, preferred. *Cyclops, Daphnia,* tubificid worms, bloodworms, etc., are all happily taken. The problem is that almost all of the corys are bottom fishes that root around in the substrate searching for food. Any aggressive or fast-moving tankmates usually will finish up the bulk of the food (or at least the best morsels) before it falls to the bottom where the corys can get it. Hungry corys will of course try their best to compete for food, even in mid-water or at the surface (upside-down at times!). Among the corys are some long-snouted forms that are better adapted to get at food more deeply hidden in

crevices or the substrate, and a few species swim off the bottom and search the surfaces of leaves for food. Corys appear to locate food by smell rather than sight. Anyone who has dropped food into a cory tank will attest that they may ignore it until they sense its presence, after which they dash about seemingly aimlessly (but apparently following some scent trail) until they locate a food item. *Corydoras* species are also reported to eat planaria (flatworms) as well as blue-green algae, thus doing a service for their owners.

Corydoras adolfoi feeding on tubifex worms. Photo by Dr. Herbert R. Axelrod.

A beautiful Amazon tank that would make an excellent home for *Corydoras*. Photo by B. Degen.

These small fishes can be housed in almost any size aquarium from about 2 1/2 gallons (for some pygmy species) on up. However, for the most part corys are social fishes and do best when kept in groups of at least 6, better yet 10 or more. Otherwise they become more stressed and therefore more prone to diseases. For the average sized cory then at least a 15- to 20-gallon tank should be used. Shallower tanks are preferred over deeper tanks as the corys do have to come to the surface for air. Bottom material should not contain any sharp edges or be too large a grain for, according to some aquarists, these catfishes have rather delicate barbels that could become damaged through abrasion. Others debate the validity of this saying the disintegration of the barbels is due to filth and disease in the tank. If undecided, it is perhaps best to keep your tank clean AND avoid sharp

edges—then you are safe on both counts. Because of the activity of these bottom rooters, good filtration is recommended or the aquarium will have consistently poor visibility. The tank should be well planted for these rather shy fishes but a clear space should be left open in the middle-front for viewing the fishes. Bunch plants are recommended along with swordplants, *Vallisneria,* *Sagittaria,* etc., to provide shelter as well as a pleasing scene for the aquarist.

Corys are very disease resistant although they are not indestructible. Fungus attacks do occur when they are kept under poor environmental conditions or given an inadequate diet. Damage can also occur when they are netted as their spines almost invariably get stuck in the

This densely planted tank could hide many *Corydoras,* which would not harm the plants. Photo by Tomey.

Corydoras trilineatus. Photo by Burkhard Kahl.

Bunch plants such as val, *Vallisneria*, provide security for the *Corydoras* while increasing the attractiveness of the tank. Photo by T. J. Horeman.

mesh. The easiest way to release a cory from a net is to invert it in the water and let it free itself. This they seem to be quite adept at.

In their natural habitat, corys generally live in shallow (less than 2 meters deep), slow-moving streams and small rivers of clear water where they tend to be found in aggregations of a few individuals to many hundreds, including males, females, and juveniles. Sometimes the aggregations even include more than one species. At night they congregate more in the quieter, shallower waters, while during the day they move to the relatively deeper water where there is a current. Corys are apparently absent from coastal regions because of their limited tolerance to salt. The preferred bottom type is sand, but areas with mixed sand and mud to pure mud substrates are also inhabited. Detritus and/or dead leaves may cover the bottom, and the stream banks commonly support a luxuriant growth of vegetation that provides shade for the shallow areas. They can also survive in swampy situations where the oxygen content is low by virtue of their ability to absorb oxygen from surface air through their gut. They make rapid darts to the surface for a gulp of air which passes through their gut and eventually is passed out through the anus. This activity can be seen in aquaria, especially if the oxygen content becomes lowered for one reason or another. Cory activity can thus be a good indication of the water quality of their tank if attention is paid to the number of times per unit of time they dart to the surface. If these trips increase in frequency dramatically, something is probably seriously wrong and the water should be tested and perhaps partially changed. The onset of the rainy season usually initiates courting behavior in corys. This is no doubt due to the

increase in food items that usually accompanies these rains, thereby providing a good supply for the fry when they hatch out. Their natural food consists of worms and insect larvae that are rooted out of the bottom mud or sand, as well as some vegetable matter. They will also take flesh from dead fishes (true scavenging) but do not actively hunt live ones.

Although *Corydoras aeneus* and *C. paleatus* are among the easiest of the species to spawn and are even bred and raised commercially, the spawning of corys is not as easy as some of the beginners' fishes among the other families of aquarium fishes. It does

Egg mass of *Aspidoras* species. Photo by Alan Pinkerton.

Even a small catfish such as *Aspidoras* species may have large eggs, although only a few may be laid. Photo by Alan Pinkerton.

take some knowledge and preparation to produce a successful spawning. With patience it can be done, however, without too much trouble. In addition to *C. aeneus* and *C. paleatus*, easily spawned species include *C. nanus*, *C. elegans*, and *C. eques*, as well as the dwarfs *C. hastatus* and *C. pygmaeus*. Moderately easy species are said to be *Corydoras trilineatus*, *C. melanistius*, *C. caudimaculatus*, and *C. bondi*. More difficult species include *C. schwartzi*, *C. arcuatus*, *C. sterbai*, *C. haraldschultzi*, and *C. barbatus*. Of course the difficulty depends a great deal upon the skills and the "luck" of the

aquarists (availability of the right type water, availability of good, healthy fishes, etc.). What might be a very difficult species to one aquarist may be rather easy to another.

The courtship behavior, spawning act, carrying and deposition of eggs on a substrate, and other aspects of cory breeding are very similar, so similar in fact that a generalized description of the spawning process can be given that should suffice for most species. In the writeups that follow, when there is an "unknown" species of *Corydoras* available, one that there is no information available for, there is reference to "normal" or "usual" conditions. These are the conditions and methods mentioned in this introductory material. Differences from this "norm" would involve things like differences in the numbers of eggs (per spawning bout or total per female), time of day of spawning, temperature for spawning, choice of substrate, choice of water level at which eggs are placed, spawning inducements, etc. There are some exceptions to the rule, however, and these will be noted under the particular species accounts when known. The spawning tank for almost all species should be at least five gallons capacity for the smallest species, 15 to 20 gallons for the average sized species. It should be well planted with bunch plants as well as broad-leaved types, the latter for reception of eggs if necessary. Java fern seems to be most preferred. The substrate should generally be dark (although some breeders advocate a bare bottom). Aeration and filtration are recommended, as are weekly water changes. Either 4-5 males with 2-3 females or two or three males per female is the proper ratio for spawning groups in most species. These can be selected from the initial group of six or more held in a community tank. Sexes are separable by even an amateur (after a little practice) by viewing the group from above. The females can be seen as being heavier across the

Large egg mass of *Corydoras aeneus*. Photo by R. Zukal.

body at the pectoral fins; when viewed from the side females may be a little deeper-bodied with a bulging ventral profile if they are full of eggs. Males occasionally have more pointed ventral fins and slightly longer dorsal and pectoral fin spines.

Inducement of spawning may involve simply separating the sexes and feeding them well on a high protein diet (this is called conditioning) until such a time as it is thought that they are ready to spawn and then placing them together in the breeding tank. Some aquarists

1. Female *Corydoras* usually are much heavier-bodied that the slender males.

2. The spawning tank must provide several good substrates to which the eggs may be attached.

3. At first, several males may chase a receptive female.

4. The female investigates many substrates to find the best one on which to attach her eggs.

swear by a water change or a temperature drop (no more than about 4 or 5 degrees) or even sprinkling water on the surface of the spawning tank to imitate the onset of the "rainy season" to initiate spawning. At least some recently imported specimens still hold to particular seasons in which they will more readily spawn. For example, from December to March seems to be a good time to try these catfishes, as is August to October. The further the fishes are in time from their old habits, the less they seem to be tied to these particular spawning seasons (which apparently coincide with the rainy seasons in their native lands). The temperature changes should, of course, be gradual to avoid stressing the fishes and possibly causing disease. Under normal conditions the corys should spawn readily.

The first hint that spawning may occur is increased activity as the females start swimming restlessly about and are

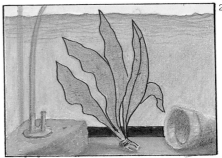

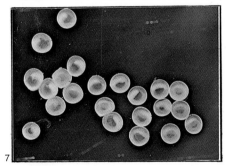

soon swarmed about and followed by the males. Normally the corys are slow moving, albeit somewhat nervous. But in pre-courtship bouts they become very active, dashing back and forth across the tank and up and down, the males usually in hot pursuit of the females. These frantic dashes are interrupted at times by the males displaying or "dancing" in front of the females, apparently trying to position themselves across the head of the females. The females may ignore these at first and continue their headlong flights with the males not far behind, but eventually they become stimulated by and interested in the males' actions and in a change of behavior start to inspect potential spawning sites. These may be anything from plant leaves to the side of the tank — anything that is flat and solid seems to fit the bill. Cleaning of several of these sites then commences, with or without the help of the males. Actually, different species have

5. The classic T-position during which eggs are laid and fertilized.

6. The female may hold as many as 10 eggs in a basket formed by her pelvic fins.

7. Eggs are firmly attached to the selected substrate batch by batch.

8. Minimal filtration ensures that young fish will not be lost.

different preferences for spawning sites, one favoring plant leaves, one favoring driftwood, one favoring the glass sides of the aquarium, etc. The majority, however, seem to prefer a site off the bottom but some distance from the surface of the water, and more likely than not some area in the vicinity of an air stone where the current is stronger. The positioning of the eggs off the bottom helps prevent some predation on the eggs by these bottom scouring fishes. The characteristic dashes to the surface for a gulp of air continue during these activities and, in fact, the frequency of these trips usually increases.

As courtship progresses contact between the spawners occurs more often with the males usually in a position above and behind the female where they can make contact with an area just behind her head. Males may also nudge or butt the

The T-position of laying and fertilization in *Corydoras aeneus*. Photo by H. J. Richter.

Occasionally eggs escape before they are attached. Notice the large size of the eggs of *Corydoras aeneus*. Photo by H. J. Richter.

females. Actual spawning is then imminent.

The early morning hours are the preferred time for cory spawning, although the timing may be different with different species. Chasing continues but with the tables turned, that is, the females now after the males. The female will often position herself so that she can nudge or press the male in his side while her barbels are very active. A male sometimes will initiate this pose by positioning his body in front of her head. In either case the male will roll over a bit and clasp the female's barbels with his pectoral spines so that they are locked in a sort of embrace. This is called the "T" position. It is possible that the serrate or rough inner edges to the male's pectoral spines help hold the female's slippery barbels. This position apparently acts as the stimulus for the release of the eggs and sperm of the partners simultaneously. The movement of the fins and the fishes themselves creates enough eddies to ensure the fertilization of most of the eggs. This position is held for as long as a minute in some species, but generally lasts about 15 seconds during which time one to as many as ten eggs are passed by the female into a pouch or basket formed by her clasped pelvic fins. It is at this time that the eggs are fertilized. Actually the T-position is not always formed and egg-laying and their fertilization are accomplished just as successfully with the partners side by side. The male then releases the female's barbels. With the eggs safely cradled in her pelvic fins the female moves off to one of the selected and pre-cleaned deposition sites (or may even decide to clean new spots). Perhaps further touching up is needed and the female may mouth the spot again, giving rise no doubt to the story that she is depositing sperm that she inhaled during the T-position. Once satisfied

that the spot is "just perfect" the female will finally open her pelvics and press the eggs against that spot. The eggs are quite sticky and adhere to glass, leaves, or whatever, very tightly. It is interesting to speculate why the eggs do not adhere to the pelvic fins themselves. Perhaps a mucus coating prevents this from happening. In some species (ex. *C. bondi bondi, C. trilineatus*) the female is said to dash madly into a plant thicket, opening her pelvic fins and releasing the eggs almost like an egg scatterer. The eggs will fall into the plants where they adhere to the plant leaves. One species of plant recommended for these species is Java moss, *Vesicularia dubyana.* Sometimes the female does not time this properly and the eggs are released before the plants are entered and they fall to the bottom where they often perish or may be eaten. Between spawning bouts the female may pause to rest or grub around for food, during which time she may find and eat some of the eggs already spawned. It has

The swollen belly of a fertile female is very obvious in this photo by H. J. Richter.

been suggested that food be made available for the spawners in the form of whiteworms or even tubificid worms, although more care must be exercised with the latter in order to prevent pollution.

Once a batch of eggs are deposited (sometimes even before the female is finished) the males are swarming about her again ready for the next spawning bout. The same procedure occurs over and over again (as many as 50 times depending upon the species) until the female signals she no longer has any eggs left and is no longer interested in continuing. Once spawning is completed, it is best to remove the parents or, conversely, remove the eggs to a hatching and rearing tank with virtually identical water conditions.

The eggs vary in size, usually about 1.0 to 2.0 mm, and are transparent or light-colored at first, but they darken as they develop and the embryo becomes more and more visible. The number of eggs, for the average species numbering in the hundreds, depends on the species, but also involves the size of the female as well as her age and condition. According to reports, *Corydoras hastatus* probably lays the fewest eggs with about 30, *C. eques* the most with approximately 800. The total number may be reduced by predation by the spawners or some of the non-spawning individuals. Well fed spawners usually ignore the eggs. Spawning usually lasts for a couple of days, the most productive of which sometimes not being the first, which often leads to a reduced count as the spawning is in fact interrupted. The aquarist, after seeing the initial deposition of the eggs, may remove the spawning fish with the mistaken idea that spawning is over and that to leave the parents in the tank would jeopardize the eggs already laid, when in truth the most productive spawning bouts were yet to come. Careful observation of the fish by the aquarist should help to avoid such mistakes as experience is gained.

Depending upon the species and the temperature, the eggs hatch in about three to eight days, most commonly four to five. It has been suggested that bright lights be avoided and a fungicide added for protection of the eggs against fungus. Good aeration near the eggs is also a good idea so that they do not lack for oxygen. Just before hatching the embryos can be seen wriggling within the egg

membrane. As they hatch out as tiny slivers they fall to the bottom where they spend the next few days living off the nourishment of their yolk sacs. After about two to three days this is about used up and they must be fed. This can initially be by infusoria, especially rotifers, which can be followed rather quickly by microworms, newly hatched brine

The female carries each batch of eggs in a basket formed by her pelvic fins. Photo of *Corydoras aeneus* by R. Zukal.

shrimp, chopped tubificid worms, and powered dry food. Growth is fairly rapid under ideal conditions. The fry are susceptible to fouled water so periodic water changes should be made. Daily water changes are advocated by some aquarists while weekly changes are recommended by others. In any case the "new" water should be aged for a few days before use. Rather than starting with a relatively small tank a 20-gallon tank is recommended in which the water level is kept low at first but increased as the fry grow so that moving them to larger quarters is unnecessary. After the first three weeks the critical period is over and losses after that will be minimal.

Properly kept corys may attain aquarium ages of five to ten years.

Although reference in the above section was almost exclusively to corys, members of the genus *Corydoras*, most of the

Infertile eggs become opaque, while fertile eggs remain relatively clear with a distinct embryo within. Infertile eggs often are attacked by water fungi. Photo of *Corydoras aeneus* eggs by H. J. Richter.

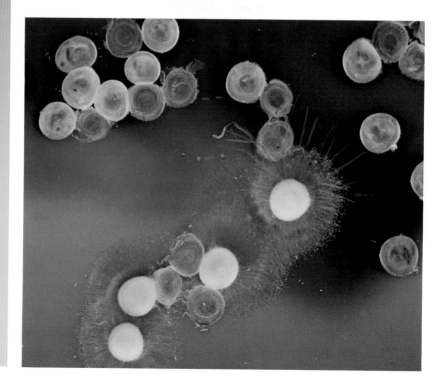

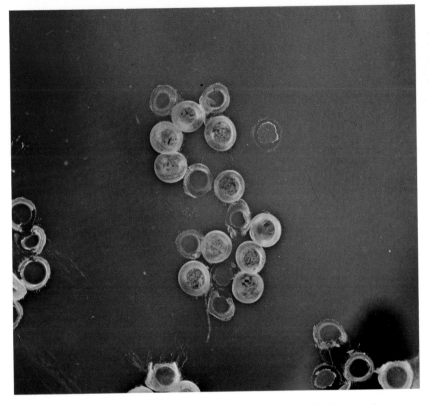

Notice the eyed embryos in these *Corydoras paleatus* eggs. Photo by H. J. Richter.

information provided can be applied to *Brochis* and *Aspidoras* as well. In addition, information included in individual writeups of a general nature may also be applicable to many of the species on which no information is available. By reading through the write-ups, the aquarist will get a general "feeling" for the conditions that should be offered the different species. Of course, knowledge of where the specimens come from would be of great utility for determining what conditions to supply, especially with regard to temperature. For example, a species from cooler mountain streams or from cooler latitudes necessarily will do better at cooler temperatures than species coming from the hot, tropical areas of Brazil. A little common sense goes a long way.

THE GENUS *ASPIDORAS*

ASPIDORAS VON IHERING, 1907

Aspidoras has recently gained some measure of popularity with aquarists. Only a few years ago there were only one or two species in the aquarium trade (perhaps more but they all seemed to be listed under the name *A. pauciradiatus*). Although this number has not increased dramatically, more species are available and, as the demand grows, even more should show up in tropical fish shops. For the most part little is still actually known about the aquarium care of most of the species except for the scattered reports on a spawning here and a spawning there. Fortunately, these little catfishes are rather accommodating and apparently can survive in captivity under normal aquarium conditions (pH 6.8-7.0; temperature 22-26°C, etc.). If they are treated much the same as the species of *Corydoras*, they should survive fairly well in hobbyist's tanks. Sexual differences can be seen in the smaller size and narrower belly of adult males.

Aspidoras pauciradiatus. Photo by Dr. H. J. Franke.

Aspidoras pauciradiatus, female. Photo by Alan Pinkerton.

Aspidoras includes about 14 species, with the type species being *A. rochai*, which hails from Fortaleza, Ceara, Brazil. In *Aspidoras*, the eyes are small, and the dorsal and pectoral spines are thickened and shortened. The character that primarily serves to distinguish this genus from the others in the subfamily is the number and shape of the cranial fontanels, *Aspidoras* possessing a small supraoccipital fossa and a small, roundish or oval to elongate frontal fontanel. In *Corydoras* and *Brochis* there is a single, open fontanel, albeit much larger and more elongate than that of *Aspidoras*, with a commisural bar anteriorly. Also, except for *A. poecilus*, all *Aspidoras* have a rounded transverse head shape as opposed to a triangularly depressed one. Some of the species of *Aspidoras* are quite similar to some of the *Corydoras* species and more than one worker in the group has suggested the synonymy of *Aspidoras* into *Corydoras*. This will probably not be accomplished in the foreseeable future. The largest species attains a length scarcely over 5 cm long. The genus is generally distributed in the Amazon region.

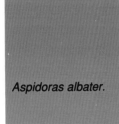

Aspidoras albater.

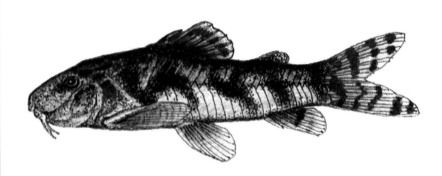

ASPIDORAS ALBATER NIJSSEN & ISBRÜCKER, 1976

This species was described from the Rio Tocantins and its tributaries in Brazil. Its primary distinguishing character is the four rather large, irregular oblique bars or blotches crossing the body. There are also some smaller, somewhat isolated spots along the back. The name *albater* was given to this fish because of this pattern, *albus* meaning white and *ater* meaning black. It is a peaceful fish that should always be kept in groups of at least 6-8 or more, which generally necessitates a tank size of about 10-15 gallons or so. It can be kept as a member of a community tank as long as its tankmates are similarly peaceful. Aggressive feeders should also be avoided as the small, shy *Aspidoras* will usually miss out on the better food items. The tank does not have to be set up in any special manner, though at least one corner should be thickly planted to provide suitable shelter because of their shyness. The bottom should consist of soft sand. The physical properties should be much the same as those for most species of *Corydoras*: pH 6.0-7.3; hardness to 20°dGH; temperature 22-24°C. This small (up to 4 cm) species is principally active during the day. It eats almost anything, but prefers living foods.

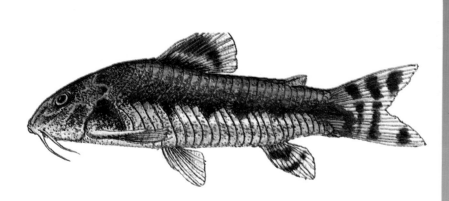

*Aspidoras
brunneus.*

ASPIDORAS BRUNNEUS NIJSSEN & ISBRÜCKER, 1976

Aspidoras brunneus is a poorly known species from Serra do Roncador, Mato Grosso, Brazil. The six original specimens used in the original description were all juveniles. There is a longitudinal dark band along the upper body that curves downward near the base of the caudal fin. The lower border of this band irregularly infringes on the light lower body color. Specimens are occasionally reported in the aquarium trade under the name *A. brunneus* but there are no assurances that the identification is correct. Nothing is known about the aquarium care, but conditions that are suitable for other *Aspidoras* species and most *Corydoras* species should be acceptable to *A. brunneus*.

Aspidoras carvalhoi.

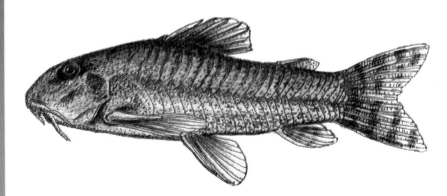

ASPIDORAS CARVALHOI NIJSSEN & ISBRÜCKER, 1976.

This species was described from Acude Canabrava, Guaramiranga, Est. Ceara, Brazil. It is poorly known and there apparently is no specific pattern in the preserved specimens, which are almost completely without chromatophores. Specimens under this name have been imported but little or no information about aquarium care and breeding is available. Conditions suitable for *Corydoras* and other *Aspidoras* species should be offered.

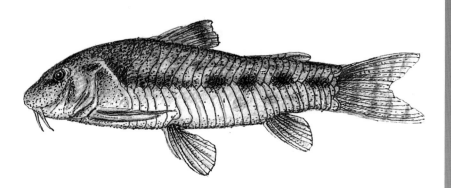

*Aspidoras
eurycephalus.*

ASPIDORAS EURYCEPHALUS NIJSSEN & ISBRÜCKER, 1976

Virtually nothing is known about this species from Corrego Vermelho into Rio das Almas, a tributary of the Rio Maranhao, Estado Goias, Brazil. The badly faded original specimens have a pattern somewhat resembling that found in *A. poecilus*. It is suggested that similar conditions as those offered other *Aspidoras* and *Corydoras* species should be tried if this species ever appears in the aquarium trade.

Aspidoras fuscoguttatus.

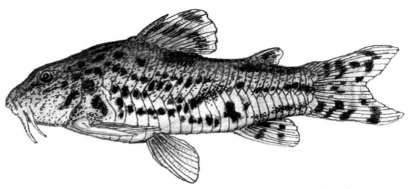

ASPIDORAS FUSCOGUTTATUS NIJSSEN & ISBRÜCKER, 1976

This species comes from Corrego Corguinho, Estradas da Tres Lagoas, Est. Mato Grosso, Brazil, and into Peru. It is recognizable by its color pattern, which consists of about four rows of spots on the anterior body that extend posteriorly and join along the midline at a level between the dorsal and adipose fins and continues as an irregular stripe to the caudal fin base. The back is dark and there is another dotted line extending along the lower body from about the middle of the pelvic fins to the lower caudal fin base. The vertical fins are variously barred or striped. A dark line extends from the eye to the snout. This is a very peaceful fish that absolutely should be kept in a school of at least six individuals. It is not a very active swimmer, but is diurnal, appearing during the daylight hours, although their tank should be somewhat darkened, perhaps by floating plants. Thus it is a very good species for a community tank of small, peaceful fishes that prefer soft water. Thickly planted aquaria of about 15-gallon capacity provided with a sand bottom, where they can dig for worms and other animals, are recommended. They accept a variety of foods but prefer live foods, such as mosquito larvae and tubificid worms. *A. fuscoguttatus* is very sensitive to abrupt changes of water conditions so care must be taken when periodic water changes are made. They prefer a pH of 5.5-6.8, a hardness up to about 12°dGH, and a temperature range of 22-25°C. These about 4 cm long fish probably spawn like *A. pauciradiatus*. The sexes are difficult to distinguish, with the females somewhat heavier than the males.

✳ ✳ ✳

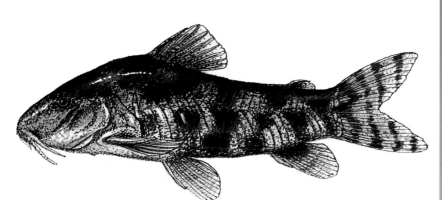

Aspidoras lakoi.

ASPIDORAS LAKOI MIRANDA-RIBEIRO, 1949

A. lakoi was originally described by Miranda-Ribeiro from Fazenda da Cachoeira, Est. Minas Gerais, Brazil. It was named in honor of Mr. Carlos Lako, who collected the first specimens. The color pattern consists of three series of four to five large spots along the body—not aligned vertically but staggered, almost in a checkerboard design. Reports of this species being imported sporadically have appeared but virtually no information on the aquarium care is available. Like other "unknowns" it is best to set up a tank similar to those that have successfully housed other *Aspidoras* species.

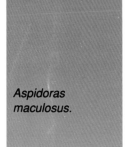

Aspidoras maculosus.

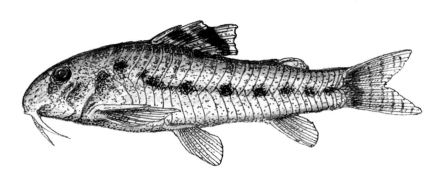

ASPIDORAS MACULOSUS NIJSSEN & ISBRÜCKER, 1976

The original specimens were collected in the Rio Paiaia, which flows into the headwaters of the Rio Itapicuru, Est. Bahia, Brazil. The name *maculosus* means "spotted" referring to the pattern of this fish. The spots are relatively small (about eye size) and not regular in shape and with much body color in between. They seem to be roughly in three horizontal series, the center one along the middle of the body with the spots a bit larger than the series above and below it. The dorsal fin has two rows of spots while the caudal has narrow vertical stripes. No aquarium information is available as this fish has not been reported in the aquarium trade. Conditions suitable for the other *Aspidoras* species should be suitable.

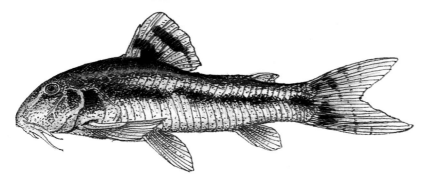

Aspidoras menezesi.

ASPIDORAS MENEZESI NIJSSEN & ISBR., 1976

The original specimens of this species were collected in the Rio Granjeiro at Crato, Estado Goias, Rio Salgado system, Brazil, by R. S. de Menezes. The species was named in honor of its collector. The most prominent feature of the color pattern is a row of large elongate blotches along the side from the gill cover to the caudal base. The posterior blotches may be united. The upper back is dusky, perhaps with some blotches or showing a marbled pattern. The lower portion of the body generally is unpigmented. The dorsal fin has some blackish markings, and the caudal fin probably is banded (it is damaged in the original specimens). This is a small (up to about 5 cm long), very peaceful,

even almost "motionless" fish that can be housed only with similar delicate species. It is not suitable for the large community tank as it will almost always be hiding. A small, 10- to 15-gallon, well-planted tank and a dark substrate, strong filtration (peat), and water surface movement are recommended, the latter because this species needs high oxygenation. In addition a pH of 6-7, a hardness no higher than 12°dGH and a temperature of 21-24°C are suggested. Like other members of its genus it prefers live foods but will accept other foods in addition. This species has successfully been spawned in captivity. The females are more round-bodied than males at spawning time and generally a little larger. No other sexual differences are known. On one occasion four pairs were placed in an 11-gallon breeding tank set up with an inside box filter, fine gravel, Java moss, and Java fern. They were conditioned primarily on live foods (tubifex and microworms). Eggs were found in the Java moss (the actual spawning was not observed), some well inside the group of plants so that the female must have had to deliberately dive into it. About 50-60 eggs, on average 2 mm in diameter, were stuck together in groups of 2-4. The adults should be removed immediately after spawning is completed for safety as they are reported to be avid egg eaters. If the eggs are to be hatched in another tank they should be removed from the spawning tank carefully and separated from each other. They should be provided with enough aeration to move them about but not enough to damage them. Water from the spawning tank should be used making sure that it is of the same temperature (25°C). At this temperature the eggs should hatch after about 4 days. The fry are approximately 5 mm long and possess a small yolk sac that disappears in about a day. The fry should be fed with microworms or some similar starting food at least twice a day. To compensate for the frequent feedings, daily water changes are recommended. In about five days after the fry have hatched out they should have doubled in size, and after three weeks they will have assumed the adult coloration. Subsequent spawns appeared on the Java moss, Java fern, and even the glass sides of the tank. The number of eggs varied, with a high of more than 200 late in the spawning season (which lasts from early December to late February). The spawning seemed to be initiated by a water change, which is not unusual in *Aspidoras* and *Corydoras* catfishes. It has been reported that this species has a habit of burying itself in sand so that at times only the top of the dorsal fin shows.

Aspidoras pauciradiatus, female. Paratype. Photo by Dr. Herbert R. Axelrod.

ASPIDORAS PAUCIRADIATUS (WEITZMAN & NIJSSEN, 1970)

Aspidoras pauciradiatus, which originally was found in the Rio Araguaia at Aruana, and later also 3,000 river kilometers away in the Rio Negro, Brazil, is perhaps the most widely imported and therefore best known member of the genus in the aquarium hobby although, as mentioned before, it is probable that other species of *Aspidoras* have entered the hobby under this name. It differs from all the other species of this genus in having only 6 soft rays in the dorsal fin, the rest having 7. One conspicuous aspect of the color pattern is the presence of a large black blotch basally on the dorsal fin. The body is decorated with about four or more rows of dark spots which tend to converge posteriorly in some specimens, almost giving the appearance of chevrons. The caudal fin, as is common in this genus, is striped. *A. pauciradiatus* is a peaceful, schooling species that is suitable for both single species tanks or community tanks with "safe" fishes such as delicate tetras and dwarf cichlids. It is not suitable for a normal community

Aspidoras pauciradiatus. Photo by Dr. H. J. Franke.

tank of larger, more frenetic species. It should be kept in a manner similar to other *Aspidoras* and *Corydoras* species. A 10- to 15-gallon tank should be provided with floating plants as a cover. Besides a temperature range of 22-25°C, a pH of about 6-7.2, and a hardness below 12°dGH, good filtration and aeration to provide oxygen-rich water and a current are recommended. Small live foods are preferred. This is a small (about 3.5 cm long), delicate, fastidious species that needs much attention in its care. It spawns in a manner similar to *A. poecilus.* Males are generally trimmer; females are quite plump when ripe with eggs. Females also have a large white area when viewed from the side. Eggs were found in some females as small as 16-23 mm

standard length. No special water conditions for breeding are needed except that a somewhat greater water circulation than for the other species should be provided. More males than females should be placed in the spawning tank. The eggs are deposited on either the glass sides of the tank or the plants. The fry hatch in about four days. After the yolk has been absorbed the usual first foods are recommended. This species caused quite a stir in the scientific community as two populations are known, living contentedly a considerable distance apart, one in the Rio Negro, the other in the Rio Araguaia. The morphological differences are not great enough to establish whether we are dealing with separate species, subspecies, or whatever.

Aspidoras poecilus.
Photo by Dr.
Herbert R. Axelrod.

ASPIDORAS POECILUS
NIJSSEN & ISBR., 1976

A. *poecilus* is an attractively marked species from the Rio Xingu, Mato Grosso, in eastern Brazil. The dorsal fin has a dark base and a dark band about a third of the way down from the outer edge. The back has large irregular dark blotches as does the postero-ventral area. Between these, along the midline, are about three dark streaks which may be bifurcated into chevrons. The caudal and anal fins are banded. This species has spawned in a 20-gallon tank which was thickly planted. The spawning group consisted of four males and three females. Spawning proceeded in a normal fashion. The eggs were found in the plants and on the glass sides of the tank, and hatched in approximately four days. The young resemble in size and appearance young *Corydoras hastatus*. Start the fry off with small live foods, for example rotifers, and a little bit later *Cyclops* can be added to the diet. Frequent water changes should be made. The recommended temperature is 28°C, which is a bit higher than the other species.

Aspidoras raimundi.

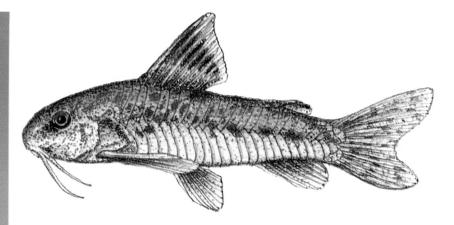

ASPIDORAS RAIMUNDI (STEINDACHNER, 1907)

Aspidoras raimundi was discovered in small creeks emptying into the Rio Parnahyba. It is readily distinguishable by the presence of a large blackish roughly triangular spot in the dorsal fin. The body is irregularly spotted and the caudal fin is banded. Apparently this species is not in the aquarium trade and no keeping information is available. Like other "unknowns" the best approach is to set up a tank as described above for other members of the genus.

Aspidoras raimundi. Photo by H. Bleher.

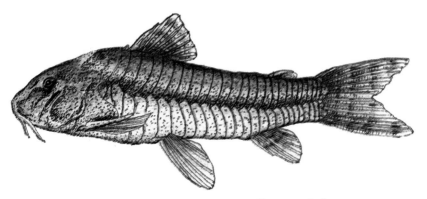

Aspidoras rochai.

ASPIDORAS ROCHAI VON IHERING, 1907

Fortaleza, the capital of Estado Ceara, Brazil, was the locality where this species was discovered. The original specimens are so faded that there is virtually no color pattern left. Fortunately, von Ihering described the pattern. There are several rounded light spots on the head and sides and a light but somewhat irregular band above the lateral line (and parallel to it) from the nape to the caudal fin base. The light band connects with the one from the other side at the nape. The dorsal fin is dark at the base and tip and light in the middle, and the caudal has several oblique series of small spots. This is a small (about 4.5 cm) peaceful schooling fish that is well suited for a community tank of small tetras and dwarf cichlids. It should not be kept with larger fishes. A 10- to 15-gallon tank that is richly planted, but with sufficient open space in the center front, is recommended. The substrate should be of sand or fine gravel. A pH of 6-7.5, a hardness of no more than 14°dGH and 6°dKH, and a temperature range of 21-25°C are suitable. *Aspidoras* love oxygen-rich water, and this species is no exception. Strong filtration and some surface movement are important. For its diet it prefers small living food, but other foods are also taken. Females can be recognized only by their heavier appearance at spawning time. This is the type species of the genus.

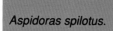

Aspidoras spilotus.

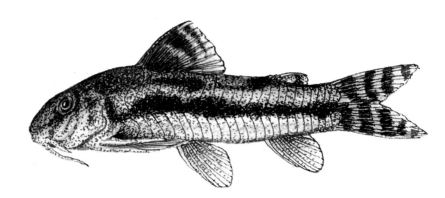

ASPIDORAS SPILOTUS NIJSSEN & ISBR., 1976

Riacho dos Macacos, a tributary of the Rio Acarau, Estado Ceara, Brazil, is the type locality of *A. spilotus*. Of more than 100 specimens the largest, the holotype, is only 3.4 cm standard length. The pattern is reminiscent of that of *A. menezesi* with a series of horizontally oval to rectangular blotches along the mid-body line ending in a spot at the base of the caudal fin. The back has a dark horizontal streak; the lower body is mostly light. The dorsal fin has a number of dark spots, mostly in the upper half, sometimes arranged in lines, and the caudal is banded. No aquarium information is available but conditions recommended for other species of the genus should be suitable to this species.

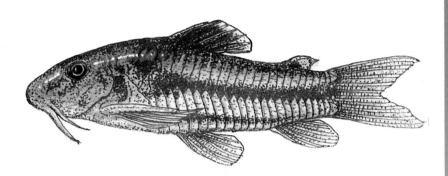

Aspidoras virgulatus.

ASPIDORAS VIRGULATUS NIJSSEN & ISBRÜCKER, 1980

The most recently described species of *Aspidoras* is *A. virgulatus* from the upper Parnahyba, Estado Maranhao, Brazil. It was discovered in samples that were misidentified as, of all things, *Corydoras treitlii*. In males enlarged odontodes (bristles) were found similar to those of *Corydoras barbatus* and other species, and distinguish this species from all other *Aspidoras*. The color pattern is also distinctive. There is a dark stripe extending along the junctures of the upper and lower lateral plates from behind the head to the base of the tail. A second, narrower stripe extends along the lower part of the body from behind the pectoral fin base to the posterior anal fin base. A hatchet-shaped mark is located on about the shoulder, the "blade" extending down in front of the mid-line stripe but separated from it, the "handle" running parallel to the mid-line stripe. The caudal fin is striped and there are some markings on the head. The same conditions that are used to keep other species of *Aspidoras* should be offered to this species.

THE GENUS *BROCHIS*

BROCHIS
COPE, 1872

The genus *Brochis* includes three species, the third species being described as recently as 1983. The type species of the genus is *Brochis splendens*. *Brochis* species look like huge *Corydoras* (especially *C. aeneus*) but differ immediately by the higher number of dorsal fin rays. Typical for the genus are 10-17 dorsal rays in comparison to 6-8 for *Corydoras*. This difference can easily be seen in aquaria so that identification to genus at least is quite simple. The behavior and aquarium requirements of both genera are also very much alike. Geographically, they are found in Brazil (upper Rio Paraguay, upper Amazon), Peru (river regions of the Rio Ucayali, Rio Maranon, and Amazon), and Ecuador (Rio Lagartococha). *Brochis* are social species that live in rain forest lakes, slow-flowing connecting channels, or in the flowing branches of silty shallow water lagoons of larger rivers. They are omnivorous, feeding on worms and insect larvae plus some vegetable matter in their natural environment, and accept readily worms, finely chopped beef heart (preferred), as well as small *Daphnia, Cyclops*, and even dried food. Like the corys and *Aspidoras* species they are peaceful and hardy fishes that are social in nature, doing best in groups or aggregations of 10 or more individuals. These undemanding diurnal fishes grow larger than species of the other genera, attaining lengths of 10 cm or more. Adult females can be distinguished only by their being somewhat larger and more rounded in the belly than are males.

Brochis britskii.
Photo by Dr. H. J. Franke.

BROCHIS BRITSKII NIJSSEN & ISBRÜCKER, 1983

This recently described species comes from the Upper Rio Paraguay, Brazil. It is most closely related to *B. multiradiatus* and similarly has a high dorsal fin count (15-18). But it also has a different head profile and body coloration and grows to a larger size (10 cm) than that species. Another essential difference is the possession of a bony shield that covers the entire underside of the head extending beyond the tip of the mental barbels. In addition, in *B. multiradiatus* the forehead

Brochis britskii. Photo by Burkhard Kahl.

at the upper side is concave, whereas in *B. britskii* it is more convex. The combination of a higher number of dorsal rays, large eyes, and short snout, however, are characteristics that an aquarist can use to distinguish it from the other two species while the fishes are being observed in their tank. Like the other *Brochis* species it is a very peaceful, diurnal, bottom living species that happily roots around the bottom of the tank for food. A 15- to 20-gallon tank should be provided and the water maintained at a temperature of 20-24°C. Small worms, mosquito and other insect larvae, and even dried foods are acceptable. It is not known if the young of this species have the large orange and black dorsal fin of the other two. Medium to small-sized *Brochis* commonly may be found swimming in the middle water layers, while adults almost always are confined to the bottom. No spawning reports are available, but this species should spawn in a manner similar to that described for *Brochis splendens*.

Brochis splendens. The top specimen came from a Peruvian river with a pH of 6.8. The bottom specimen came from more acid water (pH 5.8).

BROCHIS MULTIRADIATUS ORCES-VILLAGOMEZ, 1960

Brochis multiradiatus comes from the Upper Napo River, the eastern tributaries of the Rio Lagartococha, Ecuador, as well as Peru, the channels between the rain forest lake Yarina Cocha and the Cashibo Cocha at Pucallpa, where several examples were found in silty white water. As the name implies, the dorsal fin has a high number of rays, 17 to be more precise, which immediately distinguishes it from *Brochis splendens*, which normally has 11 or 12. The snout is also longer than that of *B. splendens* and it is often called the Hog-nosed Brochis. It differs from *B. britskii*, which also has a high number of dorsal rays (15-18), by its longer snout, smaller eye, and smaller overall size. Its aquarium care essentially is like that of the Emerald Brochis. This is a peaceful species that likes to root around on the bottom searching for food. This means that only well rooted plants (or those kept in pots?) should be used. A coarse-kernel sand bottom

Brochis multiradiatus. The male has the dorsal fin higher in front.

should predominate, but avoid sharp-angled gravel because of the digging. The aquarist must also be concerned with the water quality as this species does not do well in poor water. Water changes every 2-3 weeks of 1/2 to 2/3 should be made. A 20- to 30- gallon tank with a pH of 6-7.2, a hardness of up to 15°dGH, and a temperature of 21-24°C are recommended. *Brochis multiradiatus* eats a variety of foods (include some plant material) and is therefore no problem to the aquarist in that respect.

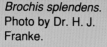

Brochis splendens.
Photo by Dr. H. J. Franke.

BROCHIS SPLENDENS (CASTELNAU, 1855)

Brochis splendens is the most commonly seen of the three *Brochis* species. It has a fairly wide distribution, including the Amazon basin in Brazil (upper Amazon, the type locality in the Rio Tocantins, and Caceres in Mato Grosso), Ecuador (Rio Napo), and Peru (Rio Ucayali, Rio Napo, Rio Maranon, and Rio Ampiyacu). It seems to prefer sluggish waters with dense vegetation along the banks, where it feeds on insect larvae, worms, and small crustaceans. Several groups were observed in tributaries of the Rio Ucayali at Pucallpa in shallow muddy waters which had a pH of 6.8-6.9, a hardness of 11°dGH, and a conductivity of 600-640 uS. At one time it was commonly known as *Brochis coeruleus*, which refers to a bluish color, but

Brochis splendens. Photo by Dr. Herbert R. Axelrod.

that name has been relegated to synonymy. The fish is currently known as the Emerald Catfish or Emerald Brochis because it also has, depending upon the light, a metallic green or blue-green color. The ventral area is yellow-ocher, with the pectoral, ventral, and anal fins also yellowish, and the dorsal and caudal a translucent brownish green. This is a schooling, peaceful fish that is very shy and retiring, and easily frightened when kept as single individuals, so must be kept in groups of at least half a dozen animals for best results. It can be kept in a community tank, however, with most not-too-large fishes as long as these tankmates are not overly aggressive nor gluttonous. It is relatively easy to keep, requiring no special conditions, and can be kept in setups similar to those for *Corydoras* species. At a length of 7 cm (males) to 9 cm (females), a tank of not less than 20 gallons is necessary. A pH of 6-6.5, a hardness to a maximum of 10°dGH, and a temperature of 22-28°C

are recommended. Soft, fine bottom material should be used. The tank should also be thickly planted and well decorated to provide sufficient hiding places. Strong filtration and partial water changes are highly recommended. This fish is not a fussy eater, but worms are definitely preferred. Like most catfishes, it takes food from the substrate. Spawning has been accomplished on a regular basis, but these spawns are often not very productive as many eggs fungus and the larvae die. The females are larger than the males, and with spawning imminent they are also somewhat heavier bodied. Their belly is said to be more pinkish in color, that of the males more yellowish. Spawning is probably seasonal or at least weather related as one spawning started after a drop in barometric pressure. In the spawning tank there should be some substrate provided as well as floating plants. *Brochis* spawn very much like the common *Corydoras* species. The activity occurs

Brochis splendens. Photo by Burkhard Kahl.

close to the bottom and may start with the males swimming over and around the females. Eventually they assume the T-position or lie side by side at which time the eggs, up to a dozen in number, are extruded and collected by the female in her pelvic fin basket. They are then pasted individually to plants (such as *Riccia fluitans*) and other objects. It was reported that two pairs produced over 1000 (900-1100) eggs of about 1.5 mm diameter. Another female produced about 830 eggs. Fortunately, the eggs are not bothered by well fed parents. At about 24°C the young hatch after 4 days and the yolk sac is absorbed in another day or two. Feed the fry with powder-fine live foods and finely chopped tubificid worms. In their first days the young react very sensitively to water deterioration and many may die at this time. As a preventative measure, the bottom should be siphoned frequently and water changes made. After about 10 days the first color (in the form of a darkish spot) develops in the middle of the body. At 18 mm (17 days) a dark cross band appears behind the head and a second runs obliquely through the eye to the tip of the snout. Five dark spots lie above the middle line and the caudal bears 2 cross bands. The conspicuously large dorsal fin is sooty-orange with white edging with a variable pattern of dark markings. After 3 weeks (21 mm long) the body pattern has become intensive, and the head and caudal bands are still evident. The characteristic uniform emerald green color develops beginning at a size of about 35 mm when the fry are 6-7 weeks old. This starts as a number of spots coalesce into a fine honeycomb pattern and the bands on the head and caudal disappear. After two months the young attain a length of 40 mm, after which they grow more slowly so that at an age of 6 months they only have a total length of between 48 and 53 mm.

THE GENUS *CORYDORAS*

CORYDORAS LACEPEDE, 1803

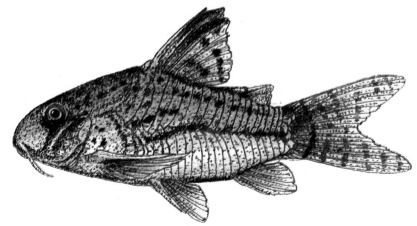

Corydoras acrensis.

CORYDORAS ACRENSIS NIJSSEN, 1972

Corydoras acrensis was discovered at Furo do Lago Sao Francisco (near the border of Peru), a tributary at the left bank of the Rio Jurua, upstream of the confluence with the Mao at Cruzeiro do Sul, Estado Acre, Brazil, by Dr. J. P. Gosse. It is a poorly known species represented only by a single specimen (the holotype) from the type locality. It was 3 cm in standard length. This species is most closely related to the sympatric *C. trilineatus* but lacks the zig-zag line at the juncture of the posterior dorsal and ventral lateral body scutes. *C. acrensis* also has a longer snout, longer dorsal fin spine, and a deeper caudal peduncle than *C. trilineatus*. Aquarium care is expected to be the same as that of *C. trilineatus*. A 15-20-gallon tank, well decorated, with near neutral pH, not too hard water, and a temperature of about 21-24°C, should be sufficient. Perhaps when it becomes better known it may turn out to be a synonym of a better known species, possibly *C. leopardus*.

Corydoras acutus. Photo by Dr. Herbert R. Axelrod.

CORYDORAS ACUTUS COPE, 1872

Corydoras acutus was described by Cope from the Shansho Cano, Rio Ampiyacu, Loreto, Peru, and apparently is distributed in northern Peru and adjacent Ecuador. It attains a length of approximately 6 cm. A well-planted and decorated tank of about 15-20 gallons is adequate. It should be given soft, slightly acid water with a temperature of 25-28°C. *C. acutus* is an omnivorous species that will accept most living and prepared foods commonly utilized for aquarium fishes. It is a peaceful fish that can be accommodated in most community tanks. This long-snouted species is recognizable by the large black blotch in its dorsal fin coupled with the dark patch (roughly triangular- or kite-shaped, and sometimes broken up into individual spots) on the anterior part of the body, the dark stripe between the upper and lower body plates posteriorly, the dusky edges to the upper body plates, and the banded caudal fin.

Corydoras adolfoi, holotype. Photo by Dr. Herbert R. Axelrod.

CORYDORAS ADOLFOI BURGESS, 1982

This species was discovered at Sao Gabriel da Cachoeira, a small tributary of the upper Rio Negro in Brazil, by Dr. Herbert R. Axelrod. It attains a size of about 4 cm standard length (6 cm including C. *imitator*), the females growing a bit larger than the males. As a social species it should be kept in groups of at least six individuals. The tank should be heavily planted around the back and sides but leaving sufficient open space in front and center to show this fish off to best advantage. Dark substrates are generally recommended. Sufficient feedings of live and frozen foods with some sinking tablets should be provided. Weekly 25% water changes are beneficial. For spawning, a ratio of two males for every female has succeeded. The pH was 6.5 and the hardness 8°dGH. New fresh water added was 2-3° cooler than that replaced, which lowered the tank water by only 1°. There was a vigorous flow from the power filter. Spawning proceeded in a typical manner, including the assumption of the T-position. A single egg (very rarely two) was deposited in the pelvic fin sac. After a few seconds rest the female proceeded to place the eggs at localities within the top two inches of the water surface; 50% within 1/2 inch of the water line (the female even had her head sticking out of the water at times to do this!). The eggs were about 25% smaller than *C. aeneus* eggs. After placing an egg in position the female rested for about two minutes (the males didn't bother her at this

Spawning adults of *Corydoras adolfoi*. Photos by Gerald R. Hickson.

Corydoras adolfoi, with the long-snouted form, *C. imitator,* in center. Photo by Dr. Herbert R. Axelrod.

time), but then all of a sudden the males started over again. The spawning lasted four to eight hours and yielded about 50 eggs. After the spawning was completed neither sex showed any more interest in the eggs. Hatching commenced early on the fifth day and continued for about 30 hours. The fry should be kept in shallow (about two inches) water with water changes three times a day. Infusoria and liquid fry food were used as the initial foods. The dark band along the back coupled with the black band through the eyes (mask) help to distinguish this species from most others. Like other "twin" corys (ex. *C. oiapoquensis/ C. condiscipulus* and *C. arcuatus/C. narcissus*) Nijssen has separated out a long-snouted form from the round-snouted form and given it a new name, *Corydoras imitator.* There is an investigation under way to determine if these long-snouted forms are indeed separate species or polyploids of the same species.

Corydoras aeneus.
Photo by Burkhard
Kahl.

CORYDORAS AENEUS (GILL, 1858)

Although described from Trinidad, C. *aeneus* appears to range over the entire Guianan plateau as well. It occurs in the small and smallest influxes to the Amazon and its tributaries, where they are mostly found in quiet, shallow waters with soft bottoms that can become very turbid when disturbed. With their intestinal respiration mechanism the low oxygen that results apparently does not cause serious problems to the fish. It reaches a length of up to 7.5 cm, the males being slightly smaller and more slender than females. This is a very easy to keep, unpretentious, productive, and easy to breed species. Like *C. paleatus*, *C. aeneus* is one of the most well-known and well loved species of *Corydoras* in the aquarium field. Being very peaceful it is well suited as a community tank fish. However, as in most cory species groups of six or more individuals are recommended. It is omnivorous, accepting a wide range of foods. Water conditions are not critical, but should not be too hard and alkaline. To get this fish to spawn is comparatively easy. A change of water or a slight increase (or in some cases even a decrease) in

Corydoras aeneus, albino. Photo by Burkhard Kahl.

Corydoras cf. *aeneus*, perhaps a geographic form. Photo by Aaron Norman.

temperature could set them off. With a number of individuals in a tank several pairs will probably spawn synchronously, as if there were some signal that precipitated the event. Males pursue the females until the females are almost ready to spawn and start to become interested in their advances. They start searching for egg deposition sites, which are cleaned assiduously. The sites in this species could be anything, the most popular being plant leaves and the glass sides of the tank; slightly less interesting seem to be rock surfaces. After courtship by the male that involves, among other things, him contacting the female's head with his barbels and rubbing his body against hers, they settle down to actual spawning. In most cases a T-position is assumed in which the male places his body in front of

and at right angles to the female. He manages to grasp the female's barbels with his pectoral fins and holds them tightly as the pair vibrates. The female holds her ventral fins together in such a way as to form a pocket or sac into which she discharges her eggs, usually only a few in number. The male releases the female and she moves about the aquarium searching for places upon which she can deposit her eggs. These may be previously cleaned spots or she may clean a totally new spot. After a brief rest the males again start their advances and another bout is begun. After about two to three hours a single female can deposit up to 200 eggs. *C. aeneus* normally does not bother the eggs and fry if they are

Corydoras aeneus, pale form. Photo by Andre Roth.

Corydoras aeneus. Spawning in this species can be very hectic, with much destruction to the landscaping. Photo by R. Zukal.

Only a few eggs are laid during one spawning bout. As in other corys, they are carried in the female's pelvic basket. Photo by R. Zukal.

Corydoras aeneus produces numerous batches of large eggs. Photo by Knaack.

Albino *Corydoras aeneus* spawn like normally colored members of the species. Photo by Padovani.

Corydoras cf. *aeneus*, the form once known as U-5, from Humaita, Brazil. Photo by Dr. Herbert R. Axelrod.

well fed but it may be judicious to remove the adults at the completion of the spawning. As they develop, the eggs become darker in color until they are dark brown. On about the fifth or sixth day hatching begins. The fry usually stay at the bottom of the tank and feed on infusoria or other available foods. When feeding commences it is advisable to start changing some of the water on a periodic basis. After about two to three weeks spawning activities may commence again. Wild caught specimens and those of the first few generations seem to prefer the winter to early spring (February to May) months for spawning but more domesticated individuals may spawn all

year 'round. In recent years a domestically developed albinistic strain has appeared on the market. According to Nijssen & Isbrücker (1980) *C. schultzei* is a synonym. Most of the plain-colored, greenish corys seen in pet shops will be *Corydoras aeneus*. It is one of those species that is identified by a combination of familiarity (it's so common one soon develops a feel for its recognition) and elimination (disposing of all other species that you are sure are NOT *C. aeneus*). It is interesting that when there are several very similar species placed together, even though you cannot distinguish them very well they have no trouble and set themselves apart in little groups.

Corydoras agassizi. Photo by B. Kahl.

CORYDORAS AGASSIZI STEINDACHNER, 1877

The range of this species includes western Brazil into Peru (upper Amazon, Nauta, Rio Ampiyacu, Rio Maranon) but it was originally described from Tabatinga, Amazonas. It attains a maximum length of 6.5 cm. Like other corys it is omnivorous, accepting all foods, including some plant material. Soft water with a neutral pH is recommended. Being more tropical in habitat it prefers warmer temperatures. C. *agassizi* is recognizable by the rows of spots, many of which are horizontally rectangular, on the body, the band through the eye, and the dark band through the pectoral fin base that extends upward to include the spine and anterior ray(s) of the dorsal fin. The caudal fin is barred. It is perhaps most difficult to distinguish from C. *ambiacus*, which has a very similar pattern but the dark shoulder bar does not seem to extend as far ventrally as in C. *agassizi*; in addition, the dark marking in the dorsal fin is usually confined to the first two rays in C. *agassizi*.

Corydoras amapaensis. Photo by Dr. H. J. Franke.

CORYDORAS AMAPAENSIS NIJSSEN, 1972

Originally discovered at Cachoeira Creek, at the right bank of the Rio Amapari, State of Amapa, Brazil, *C. amapaensis* also occurs in other streams in Estado Amapa as well as in the Oyapok River system in French Guiana. Specimens from the two countries differ in that those from the Amapari system always have a large brown to blackish area on the dorsal part of the body and scarcely any dark pigment in the dorsal fin; those from the Oyapok system mostly lack the dark on the body but have black pigment on the dorsal fin. In both populations, however, there is considerable variability, even in a single creek. *C. amapaensis* possesses three pairs of rictal barbels as in *C. octocirrus* and *C. septentrionalis*. However, it has a longer snout and a narrower interorbital width than *C. septentrionalis*, and lacks the prolonged pectoral spines of *C. octocirrus*. In addition, *C. amapaensis* has a mask that the other two species lack. This species should be kept in groups of at least a half dozen specimens in a 15- to 20-gallon tank. The temperature should be in the range of 22-26°C. Feeding is no problem with this omnivorous species as it will accept a variety of foods. *C. amapaensis* attains a standard length of about 5.7 cm.

Corydoras ambiacus. Photo by Dr. Herbert R. Axelrod.

CORYDORAS AMBIACUS COPE, 1872

C. ambiacus is from the Rio Ampiyacu in Peru. The original specimens were caught in a small feeder of the Ampiyacu, a tributary to the middle Rio Ucayali near Jenaro Herrara, Departamento Loreto. Conditions there were pH 6.4, 4.5°dGH, and a conductivity of about 170 uS. This is another friendly species that does best in groups in a tank of about 15-20-gallon capacity set up with a peat filter and some current. The substrate should be of a dark sand. The proper pH is about 6-7, the hardness to 10°dGH, and the temperature on the low side at 21-24°C. As for the diet, there is no problem as even dried and tablet foods are acceptable, although live foods (*Daphnia* and mosquito larvae), as well as frozen and fresh fish foods, are preferred. Unfortunately, at present there are no breeding reports. The species should, however, be spawned in extremely soft water. No color differences between the sexes have been observed. *C. ambiacus* grows to a length of about 6 cm. This species belongs to the *C. punctatus* group. It is most closely related and similar to *C. agassizi.* In addition to the differences noted under *C. agassizi,* the species presented here also has a shorter head.

Corydoras amphibelus.

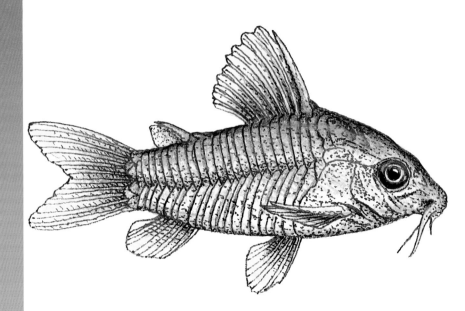

CORYDORAS AMPHIBELUS COPE, 1872

This is a very poorly known species that was described using a single specimen from the Rio Ampiyacu near Pebas, Loreto, Peru. According to Cope's original description,

"Color light olive, face with blue reflections. Numerous small black dots on the side shields, which are only wanting on the middle line of the side. Dorsal with a black spot on the ends of its radii, and another at the base of its spine. Caudal with four vertical cross-bars."

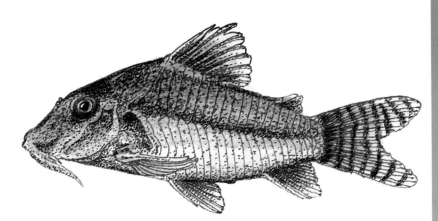

*Corydoras
approuaguensis.*

CORYDORAS APPROUAGUENSIS NIJSSEN & ISBRÜCKER, 1983

This species received its name from the locality where it was first discovered, Rio Approuague, French Guiana. It attains a length of about 7 cm. At present there have been no reports of its being in the aquarium trade so no information on how best to keep the species is available. The standard *Corydoras* conditions can be tried.

Corydoras araguaiaensis. Photo by Dr. H. J. Franke.

CORYDORAS ARAGUAIAENSIS SANDS, 1989

Another recently described and controversial species, this spotted cory from the Rio Araguaia, Brazil, is very similar to *Corydoras haraldschultzi.* It is thought to differ by details of the head pattern: black dots in *C. araguaiaensis* and black reticulations in *C. haraldschultzi.* Unfortunately such distinctions often are hard to make, and many fish don't fall well into either category. Only future research on natural populations will tell if the species are real or just variations on a color pattern of one species.

Corydoras arcuatus. Photo by Burkhard Kahl.

CORYDORAS ARCUATUS ELWIN, 1939

Corydoras arcuatus comes from the Amazon region above the city of Teffe. It attains a maximum size of up to 5 cm. Lüling observed spawning-ready pairs in shallow water of the Rio Pacaya, a tributary of the lower Rio Ucayali in eastern Peru (Lüling, *AT,* 1961, p. 33). *C. arcuatus* is quite distinctive with its dark band extending through the eye to and including the lower edge of the caudal fin. It resembles somewhat *C. narcissus* but *C. narcissus* has a less well defined band that lies higher on the back, is more tan on the head than gray, and has a peculiar concave snout (the snout is rounded in *arcuatus*). This species has been bred in captivity in a manner similar to that given in the general discussion. Standard conditions were used.

Corydoras armatus. Photo by Harald Schultz.

CORYDORAS ARMATUS (GUENTHER, 1868)

Günther originally described this fish from Xeberos (=Jeberos) on the Huallaga, Peru, as *Callichthys armatus*. It attains a length of about 6 cm (5 cm standard length). It resembles *C. loretoensis* (the differences between the two are discussed under that species).

Corydoras atropersonatus. Photo by Burkhard Kahl.

CORYDORAS ATROPERSONATUS WEITZMAN & NIJSSEN, 1970

C. atropersonatus comes from northern Peru and Ecuador (Pastaza and Loreto). It attains a length of about 5.5 cm (4.5 cm standard length). This is a very friendly species that does best in small groups in a species tank. It could also be kept with other delicate fishes or, since it is a diurnal species, with larger, friendly nocturnal catfishes such as *Hypostomus* or *Peckoltia*. The tank should have about 15 to 20 gallons capacity and be well planted. The substrate should consist of fine sand, never with gravel that has sharp angles. The water itself should be soft (hardness 4-8°dGH), with a pH of 6-7, and a temperature of 21-24°C. A mild current should be provided along with good filtration. Water changes are necessary as this species is very sensitive to nitrate-containing water. Although preferring live foods, frozen, flake, and tablet foods are readily accepted. Until now there have been no reports about the spawning of this species. *C. atropersonatus* is very close to *C. sychri* but appears to have a shorter head, shorter snout, a larger eye, and a deeper caudal peduncle. There are also indications of one or two bands in the dorsal fin that are missing in *C. sychri.*

Corydoras axelrodi.
Photo by Dr. H. J.
Franke.

CORYDORAS AXELRODI RÖSSEL, 1962

Rio Meta, Colombia, is the home of *C. axelrodi*. This species attains a maximum length of about 5 cm. It is omnivorous, accepting all types of foods, but preferring live foods. *C. axelrodi* is easily recognizable by its eye bar and the dark band that extends from the origin of the lateral line to the lower tip of the caudal fin, combined with a secondary band below the anterior part of this band that extends posteriorly only a relatively short distance. There is a hint of another stripe between these two but it often merges with the main band. The base of the dorsal fin is sooty, the color continuing along the back to the end of the caudal peduncle. This species can be kept successfully under normal *Corydoras* conditions. No reports are available regarding spawning success but this may only be because the species is not always common in the aquarium trade.

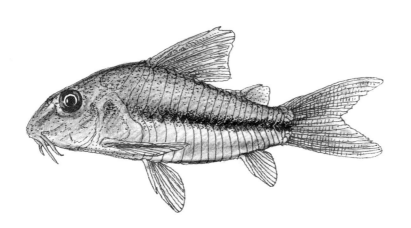

Corydoras baderi.

CORYDORAS BADERI
GEISLER, 1969

C. baderi occurs from the Rio Paru do Oeste, Para, Brazil, where Bader's specimens were from, to the Marowijne River in Surinam, where in the next year Nijssen described it again as *C. oelemariensis*, apparently unaware of the Geisler species. The color pattern resembles somewhat that of *C. bondi* but *C. baderi* lacks the spotted pattern of that species. It also resembles *C. nattereri*, which seems to have a uniform stripe, whereas in *C. baderi* the stripe is weaker anteriorly. Because this species is not readily recognized there are few reports in the aquarium literature under this name. It is expected to do well in the normal conditions provided for most other species of *Corydoras*.

Corydoras barbatus. Photo by Burkhard Kahl.

CORYDORAS BARBATUS (QUOY & GAIMARD, 1824)

This unusual species comes from southeastern Brazil, in the region from Santos (Sao Paulo) to Rio de Janeiro. Besides being one of the prettiest it is one of the largest of the *Corydoras* species, the maximum size attained being about 12 cm although it seems to reach a somewhat smaller size (about 8.5 cm) when kept in captivity. The body also is somewhat more elongated than most *Corydoras*. Being very peaceful, this is a good community tank fish, although it prefers to dig in the bottom substrate in search for food and virtually buries itself at times. This keeps the bottom stirred up a bit and there is a need for a good filtration system. Although this species comes from southern Brazil it should be kept slightly warmer than most corys (up to 28°C). Spawning has been accomplished but only with difficulty. On one occasion the spawning conditions included a pH of 7.0, a hardness of 18°dGH, and a temperature of 24°C. Sexual dimorphism is quite striking in comparison to most other *Corydoras* species. In the males the first pectoral fin ray is very long and blackish. Also the edge of the head in males is provided with short bristles (hence the species name = bearded). The spawners (5 males, 7 females) were on average 6 cm long. The spawning procedure differs from other *Corydoras* species in that the females actively drive the males and dash back and forth a great deal. According to some reports as the sperm are released the female sinks to the bottom, resting on one of her elongate pectoral fins

while she starts fanning with the other pectoral fin. At this time some eggs are released which fall into the pelvic fin basket and are apparently fertilized at that time. The eggs are then fastened, mostly in dense clusters, in the vicinity of the water's surface. In this instance during the next 12 to 15 hours about 60

Head of a male *Corydoras barbatus* showing the bristles or beard. Photo by Dr. Herbert R. Axelrod.

Corydoras barbatus. Photo by Dr. Herbert R. Axelrod.

eggs (perhaps only by one female) were fastened to the aquarium glass near the surface in bunches of up to 3-4 eggs. Between these bouts of egg-laying the animals swam about in the open in the middle water layers, the males displaying by positioning themselves broadside in front of the females. Of the first 60 eggs, 56 fry hatched after about 5 days, of which, however, about 25% died. After about two days the fry, about 7 mm long, were fed frozen rotifers. Two weeks later they were able to eat live newly hatched brine shrimp and grew very rapidly. The sexes were still not yet distinguishable by the time they attained a length of 4 cm.

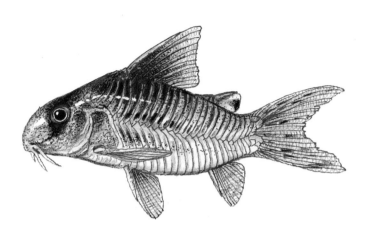

Corydoras bicolor.

CORYDORAS BICOLOR NIJSSEN & ISBRÜCKER, 1967

This poorly known little (2.5-2.6 cm) species was described from the Sipaliwini River, Surinam, near the Brazilian border. Most of the known specimens are immature.

From *Corydoras melanistius* it differs in lacking pigment spots on the head and body, the body coloration consisting mostly of a dark blotch under the dorsal fin plus a mask through the eye. *Corydoras burgessi* is very similar but has the dorsal fin largely black.

Corydoras blochi vittatus.

CORYDORAS BLOCHI NIJSSEN, 1971

This species was divided into two subspecies, the first being C. *blochi blochi*, from the Amazonas, Branco, Orinoco, and Essequibo drainages, and C. *blochi vittatus*, from the Rio Itapicuru drainage in Brazil. They differ chiefly in color pattern, *blochi vittatus* having a horizontal stripe along the posterior part of the body that *blochi blochi* lacks, while *blochi blochi* has vertical stripes in the caudal fin that *blochi vittatus* lacks. Both subspecies attain a length of about 6 cm. This is a rarely imported species and very little is known about its care and breeding. It should follow the pattern and accept the same conditions as the majority of other *Corydoras* species.

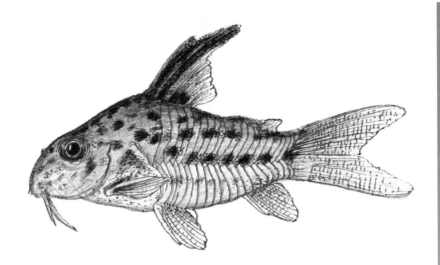

*Corydoras
boehlkei.*

CORYDORAS BOEHLKEI NIJSSEN & ISBRÜCKER, 1982

This species was described on the basis of three specimens from Rio Cuchime, Edo Bolivar, Venezuela. These were collected by Dr. James E. Boehlke and Mr. William G. Saul and sent to Drs. Nijssen and Isbrücker for final determination as to whether or not they represented a new species. In the interim Dr. Boehlke passed away. With the permission of Mrs. Eugenia B. Boehlke the species was named in her husband's honor, as it indeed turned out to be new. Unfortunately, the specimens were immature, the largest 2.6 cm standard length. The combination of comparatively large spots on the head and the body, the lack of a mask and stripes on the caudal fin, and the presence of black coloration on the anterior rays of the dorsal fin, distinguish this species. Since it apparently is not yet in the hobby nothing is known about the care and breeding of this species. It is expected to behave similar to other cory species.

Corydoras boesemani.

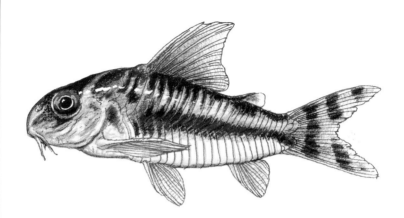

CORYDORAS BOESEMANI NIJSSEN & ISBRÜCKER, 1967

Corydoras boesemani is distributed in Surinam (Gran Rio; Corantijn). It is distinctively patterned with a broad black band along the middle of the body, dark spots along the back, the anterior rays of the dorsal fin black, and a black band crossing the caudal fin with another crossing the lobes. It apparently is not available in the aquarium trade so information about care and breeding is lacking. The standard conditions for keeping *Corydoras* should be tried if this species becomes available.

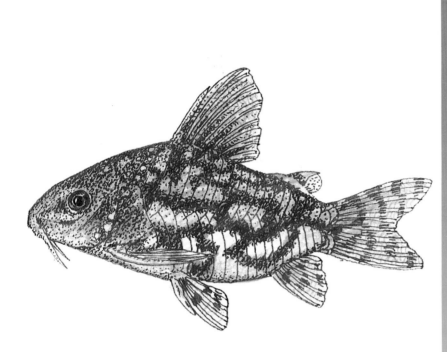

Corydoras bolivianus.

CORYDORAS BOLIVIANUS NIJSSEN & ISBRÜCKER, 1983

This species was collected some kilometers from the city of Trinidad, Rio Mamore basin, Bolivia. It attains a length of about 7 cm (5.8 cm standard length). This species differs from the similarly patterned C. *reticulatus* by having a patterned dorsal fin, not a large black spot as in *reticulatus*. The care and breeding are similar to that of the other *Corydoras* species.

Corydoras bondi.
Photo by Dr. H. J.
Franke.

CORYDORAS BONDI GOSLINE, 1940

Corydoras bondi was split into two subspecies by Nijssen in 1970, *C. bondi bondi* Gosline originating from the Rio Yuruari in Venezuela, and *C. bondi coppenamensis* Nijssen from the Coppename River, Saramacca District, Surinam. *C. bondi coppenamensis* differs from *C. bondi bondi* chiefly by having "circular spots on the head and dorsal part of the body instead of irregularly formed spots on head and body for *C. bondi bondi*." *C. b. coppenamensis* also has a larger dorsal fin spine. This is a peaceful species about 4 cm long that remains quite small and therefore is suitable for a community tank. Water conditions for one spawning included a pH of 7.2, a hardness of 12°dGH, and a temperature of 28°C. Relatively few eggs, mostly two at a time per pairing, are deposited almost exclusively in Java moss during the early morning hours. On rare occasions some eggs may also be placed on the glass sides. A total of about 30 eggs was found. These hatched in 5 days. They seemed to grow quite slowly in spite of feedings of living or frozen rotifers and *Artemia* nauplii. Later spawns yielded up to 70 young catfish per female. This species should become more available to the aquarium hobby with more successful spawnings.

Corydoras bondi. Photo by Dr. H. J. Franke.

Corydoras burgessi. Photo by Dr. Warren E. Burgess.

CORYDORAS BURGESSI AXELROD, 1987

This species, named after yours truly, was discovered in the Rio Unini, a tributary of the Rio Negro, Amazonas, Brazil. The specimens were collected in brown water as contrasted with the black water of the nearby Rio Negro. The species attains a length of about 6 cm (4.8 cm standard length). It seems to be most closely related to C. *bicolor* from the Sipaliwini River, Surinam, but differs from that species in counts and measurements as indicated in the original description. Also, the dorsal blotch seems to extend further into the fin in C. *burgessi*. Not much is known about the care and breeding of this recently described species, but specimens are becoming more common and there should be breeding reports available in the near future. Until then the same conditions that are successful with other cory species should be tried.

Corydoras burgessi. Photo by Dr. H. J. Franke.

Corydoras burgessi. Photo by Burkhard Kahl.

Corydoras carlae.

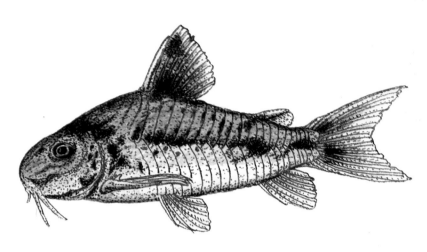

CORYDORAS CARLAE NIJSSEN & ISBRÜCKER, 1983

Corydoras carlae is a poorly known species described on the basis of two specimens, 4.2 and 3.5 cm in standard length, from the left bank of the Rio Iguazu, Parana basin, Argentina. It has not yet been imported for the aquarium trade and no information on keeping and breeding this fish is available. Being from Argentina it is expected that cooler temperatures might work better than warmer ones. Otherwise similar conditions as for other *Corydoras* species should prevail.

CORYDORAS CAUDIMACULATUS RÖSSEL, 1961

C. caudimaculatus comes from the upper Rio Guapore, Brazil (on the border with Bolivia). It attains a maximum length of about 5.5 cm. An attractive species similar to *C. guapore*, it is, however, somewhat more robust and more peaceful. Like many other corys it is quite suitable for a community tank. A tank size of 15 to 20 gallons capacity can be used to house a group of *C. caudimaculatus*. The bottom substrate should be of fine sand. A temperature range of 22-26°C is recommended, otherwise keep it as you would *C. guapore*. It is somewhat more tolerant to water conditions than that species, but it is still no species for the beginner.

Corydoras caudimaculatus. Photo by Dr. H. J. Franke.

Clear, nitrate-free, well filtered water with regular water changes every 3-4 weeks and regular filter cleaning and maintenance are recommended. Food is no problem and it will accept almost anything, even tablet food. Naturally, every species prefers live food. Spawning has been accomplished in captivity. At least newly imported individuals seem to have a definite spawning season which extends over 3 1/2 months. In one report of a group spawning over a period of 10 days approximately 1800 eggs were deposited, out of which more than 50% hatched. Unfortunately, out of these very few were actually raised. The eggs are adhesive and approximately 2 mm in diameter. Two days after hatching they begin to feed. They grow very slowly. Other reports also have them as being difficult to raise. Perhaps some conditions are not quite right or they are not receiving the particular food that they need. It is hoped that spawning methods will be perfected soon so that this species will appear more commonly in pet shops.

Corydoras caudimaculatus. Photo by Dr. Herbert R. Axelrod.

CORYDORAS CERVINUS RÖSSEL, 1962

C. *cervinus* was described from only two specimens imported for the aquarium trade. These original specimens were collected in the main stream of the upper Rio Guapore, Rondonia, Brazil, by Harald Schultz. It attains a length of 6 cm (4.9 cm standard length). According to Rössel, C. *cervinus* is most closely related to C. *treitlii* and C. *fowleri*. C. *treitlii* has a smaller eye, a longer caudal, and shorter fin spines. The barbels of C. *treitlii* are also longer and thicker. C. *fowleri* has a narrower body, the snout is longer, and the eye somewhat smaller. Besides, the color pattern of C. *cervinus* differs from both those species. Occasional specimens are seen from time to time but it is never common in the aquarium trade. There are no reports available on the keeping and spawning of this species but it should be amenable to conditions that house other corys.

Corydoras cervinus.

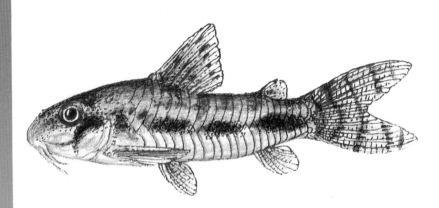

Corydoras cochui.

CORYDORAS COCHUI MYERS & WEITZMAN, 1954

C. cochui was collected in the Rio Araguaya (Goiaz Province), Santa Maria Novo, Brazil. It is one of the smallest corys, with a maximum size of only about 2.5 cm, and should be given the smallest live foods. Other foods are accepted provided they are sufficiently small. *C. cochui* was successfully spawned in 1984, although the spawning itself was not observed. The pH was 7.0, the hardness less than 18°dGH, and the temperature 26°C. About 14 eggs were attached to the Java moss, to the filter, and to the glass sides of the aquarium. On the fourth day 7 young appeared. After a week 23 more eggs were discovered of which 16 hatched. Feeding was performed as described in *C. barbatus*. This species was named for the collector, Mr. Fred Cochu. It is close to *C. paleatus* but differs in the narrower interorbital space, more slender form, and different color pattern.

CORYDORAS CONCOLOR WEITZMAN, 1961

C. concolor was collected by Dr. A. Fernandez-Yepez at Las Mangas, in a tributary of the Rio Parguaza, Estado Bolivar, Venezuela. Other specimens were collected in the Rio Parguaza itself. It is a species without dark markings, therefore resembling *C. aeneus*, but *C. concolor* has a deeper body, larger eye, and taller dorsal fin spine. Another plain cory, *C. latus*, has a shorter snout and shorter dorsal fin spine. The lack of a pattern prompted the name *concolor*. This species is only rarely seen in the hobby and reports on the keeping and breeding are not available, though these are expected to be similar to other species of cory.

Corydoras concolor.

*Corydoras
condiscipulus.*

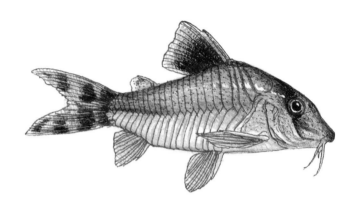

CORYDORAS CONDISCIPULUS NIJSSEN & ISBRÜCKER, 1980

This species was collected in the Oyapok and Camopi Rivers and environs of French Guiana. It is interesting that the holotype and some of the paratypes of *C. condiscipulus* were actually part of the type series of *C. oiapoquensis* as has happened in the species pair of *C. adolfoi* and *C. imitator*. As mentioned before, confirmation of the distinction of these species is being questioned and under investigation by molecular biologists. The specific name reflects this togetherness for the Latin translates as schoolmate. *C. condiscipulus* differs from *C. oiapoquensis* basically by the concave snout of the former as compared to a rounded snout in the latter. Aquarium care and breeding have not been reported but nothing unusual is expected and normal aquarium conditions should suffice.

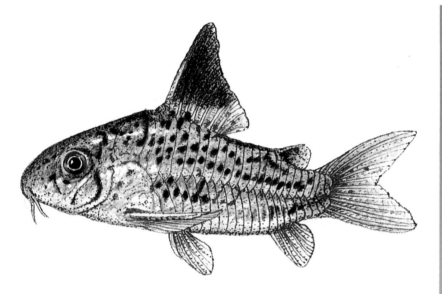

Corydoras copei.

CORYDORAS COPEI NIJSSEN & ISBRÜCKER, 1986

This species was described on the basis of only five specimens collected in the lower course of the Rio Huytoyacu, a right bank tributary to the Rio Pastaza in Peru. For best results keep at least six individuals together in at least a 15- to 20-gallon aquarium. The temperature should be about 22-25°C. This peaceful species can be kept in a community tank. It grows to a length of about 5 cm. This is another species that is rare in the aquarium trade and very little has ever been written about it. Fortunately, most corys are very tolerant and normal aquarium conditions should be adequate for keeping and even breeding.

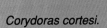

Corydoras cortesi.

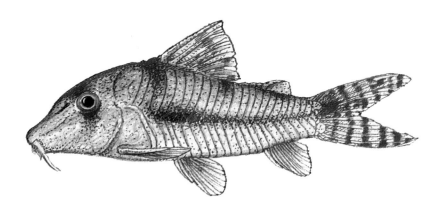

CORYDORAS CORTESI CASTRO, 1987

This newly described Colombian species is from the Rio Arauca near Arauca. It reaches about 4 cm in length. Virtually identical in appearance to the Venezuelan *Corydoras septentrionalis*, it differs mainly in having a dark pattern in the dorsal and caudal fins (absent in *C. septentrionalis*) and in details of counts and proportions. *Corydoras simulatus* lacks the dark band along the midside found in *C. cortesi*. It is possible that specimens of *C. cortesi* have been imported under the names of its relatives.

Corydoras davidsandsi. Photo by Hans J. Mayland.

CORYDORAS DAVIDSANDSI BLACK, 1987

This currently popular but controversial catfish may be a synonym of *Corydoras metae* or *C. melini.* It has a solid middorsal black stripe that extends from the front of the dorsal fin across the base of the caudal fin and continued (though fainter) into the lower caudal lobe. This extension of the stripe into the caudal lobe distinguishes it from the shorter-bodied *C. metae,* while *C. melini* has two black stripes along the middorsal area enclosing a clean golden stripe behind the dorsal fin.

Corydoras delphax.
Photo by Hans
Joachim Richter.

CORYDORAS DELPHAX NIJSSEN & ISBRÜCKER, 1983

C. delphax comes from the Rio Inirida system, Colombia. It is a friendly, robust species, suitable for community tanks. It can be housed under almost any tank conditions as long as the water is not too dirty. The water should, however, not be too hard (to 25°dGH). A larger tank is recommended, perhaps a 20- to 25-gallon size with a temperature in a range of 21-26°C. *C. delphax* spawns in typical *Corydoras* style. Besides the general sexual differences in size and girth, males usually have a stronger pattern. Food is no problem for this omnivorous feeder. *C. delphax* grows to a length of about 6cm.

Corydoras ehrhardti. Photo by the author.

CORYDORAS EHRHARDTI STEINDACHNER, 1910

This species was discovered in mountain streams near Joinville in Estado Parana, and Jaragua, Estado Sao Paulo, in southern Brazil. It should be kept as other species of the genus, however a cooler tank (temperature range of 19-22°C) with a strong filter current may be beneficial. In nature it feeds preponderantly on insect larvae; in the aquarium, however, it eats everything. No spawning reports are available. Socially, *C. ehrhardti* is typical of other *Corydoras*. It is very similar in general appearance to *C. paleatus* and the two species are sometimes confused. The body of *C. ehrhardti* is, however, more slender, the dark pigmentation more notable, and it remains somewhat smaller with a maximum length of 5 cm.

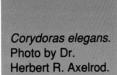

Corydoras elegans.
Photo by Dr.
Herbert R. Axelrod.

CORYDORAS ELEGANS STEINDACHNER, 1877

C. elegans comes from the Central Amazon region near Tefe and the Rio Ampiyacu, Brazil. It is one of the more inconspicuous species that is not commonly kept by aquarists. It is also the only species of the non-dwarfs (approximate maximum size is 5 cm) that prefers to swim about in the middle water layers rummaging around the plants like *C. hastatus*.

Spawning is apparently easily accomplished. More males than females (10 males per 3 females has been suggested) should be added to a spawning tank. In a report by Knaack, male *C. elegans* became territorial during prespawning activities, setting up shop in various flower pots in the tank; the females were usually hidden among the plant roots. Conditioning food included *Daphnia*, whiteworms, Grindal

*Corydoras elegans.
Photo by Dr.
Herbert R. Axelrod.*

worms, and tubificid worms. Females became constantly pursued by males, who tried to lure them into one of the "occupied" pots. Knaack reduced the population to 3 males and one female as battles became too furious. Cleaning began on the underside of plant leaves by both sexes. The spawning period lasted for more than seven weeks, the fish spawning every fourth day. Eggs were fastened under the leaves (for example *Cryptocoryne* leaves), where the cleaning had taken place, but they were also attached to roots and the glass sides of the tank. Up to 350 eggs of about 1.2 mm diameter were laid. At 24-25°C hatching occurred after 3 to 4 days. The eggs were of a yellow color at first but became darker with development. The young at the time of hatching were relatively small, however after a year they should already be sexually ripe. The first juvenile color stage greatly resembles the young of *C. hastatus* and requires the same initial food as that species. The initial feeding should be rotifers, later finely chopped tubifex can be added to establish a rapid growth rate. By the second juvenile stage (at about 13 mm length) a dark horizontal stripe appears on the sides. At this stage there is a spot in the dorsal fin but that disappears later and gives way to a series of bands. Sexual maturity is attained after 9-11 months.

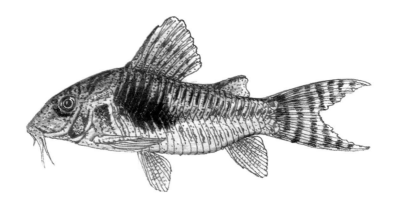

Corydoras ellisae.

CORYDORAS ELLISAE
GOSLINE, 1940

   C. ellisae was found in mountain rills at Arroyo Pona, Sapucay (Rio Paraguay system near Asuncion), Paraguay. This pointed snouted species is recognizable by the roughly diamond-shaped dark mark behind the head, the smudge of dark on the midbody below the adipose fin, and the barring of the dorsal and caudal fins. It resembles *C. acutus* somewhat but does not have the black marking in the dorsal fin of that species. This species is uncommon in the aquarium trade and little or no information is available on its keeping and breeding. Similar conditions for other *Corydoras* species should be proper.

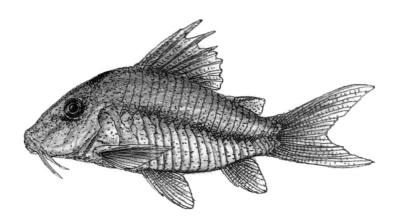

Corydoras ephippifer.

CORYDORAS EPHIPPIFER NIJSSEN, 1972

This species was discovered in creeks on either bank of the Rio Amapari, Amapa, Brazil. It grows to a size of about 5 cm. The black blotch at the base of the dorsal and extending onto the body resembles that of *C. ambiacus* but *ambiacus* has a prominently spotted body whereas *C. ephippifer* has only irregularly distributed spots. The aquarium conditions for *C. ephippifer* should be the same as that of *C. ambiacus*.

Corydoras cf. *eques*. Photo by Paysan.

CORYDORAS EQUES STEINDACHNER, 1877

The Golden-eared Cory was collected during the Thayer Expedition in 1865 near Tefe and Cudajas in the Brazilian Amazon. It grows to a length of approximately 5.5 cm. The brilliant emerald-green gill covers and iris are very attractive. Like other corys they do better in a school of 10 or more animals. The tank should be about 20 gallons capacity, well-planted, and with a soft, dark bottom substrate. The tank illumination should not be too bright so perhaps some floating plants can also be used for shade. The water should be of soft to average hardness, the pH should be neutral to slightly acid, and the temperature 24-26°C. It is not at all particular about its diet and will accept most aquarium fare. Being a peaceful species it can

Corydoras cf. *eques*. Photo by Dr. Herbert R. Axelrod.

cohabit with other species of cory. According to Knaack *C. eques* is one of the most prolific of all the *Corydoras* species with up to 800 eggs per spawning. According to Palika, however, it is not easily spawned. He says 3-5 females and 10-15 males should be placed in the spawning tank for best results. Males are shorter and more slender. Increase the temperature to 25-28°C. When there is a drop in atmospheric pressure drop the temperature to 15-19°C by adding cool water. This should be done toward evening so that spawning will take place at night. The actual spawning act is typical of the genus. Approximately 350-400 eggs per female were deposited. They were amber-colored and 1.25 mm in diameter. For the best egg development Palika suggests 3°dGH hardness and a pH of 6-6.5. The first fry hatch out in approximately two days, and begin to feed in another 2-3 days.

Corydoras esperanzae.

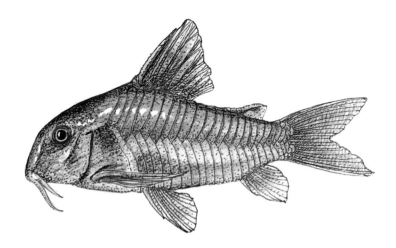

CORYDORAS ESPERANZAE CASTRO, 1987

This moderate-sized (5 cm) species was described from Cano Orocue at Orocue, Rio Meta, Colombia. It is a plain species with scattered dark pigment on the sides, heavier on top of the head; the fins are weakly patterned. Apparently *C. esperanzae* is almost identical in pattern to *C. guianensis*, differing mostly in details of counts and proportions. Additionally, at 5 cm *C. esperanzae* seems to be larger than the 4 cm *C. guianensis*.

Corydoras evelynae.

CORYDORAS EVELYNAE RÖSSEL, 1966.

This species was discovered in the upper Rio Solimoes, Amazonas, Brazil, by Dr. Herbert R. Axelrod, and named in honor of his wife Evelyn. It was described from a single specimen and attains a length of almost 5 cm. The color pattern is distinct, particularly the row of rectangular spots in a line along the upper back, and should not be confused with any other known species. Very few are imported and there is little information regarding its keeping and breeding. However, normal *Corydoras* conditions are sufficient for most of the "unknowns" and should be tried in this case as well if specimens should become available.

Corydoras filamentosus.

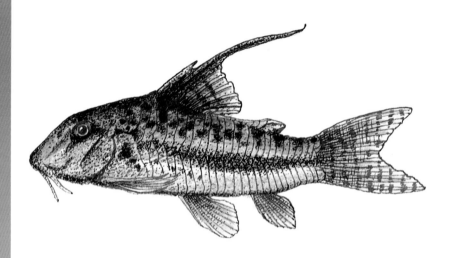

CORYDORAS FILAMENTOSUS NIJSSEN & ISBRÜCKER, 1983

This species comes from a shallow (depth 0-1 meter) affluent of Sisa Creek, Rio Corantijn basin, Nickerie district, Surinam. It appears to be a relatively small species with the original standard length recorded as 3.15 cm. The elongate filament in the dorsal fin (from which came the species name *filamentosus*) is distinctive. The color pattern also reminds one of *C. bondi*, but in *bondi* the anterior dorsal rays are not black. This species has not yet been imported through the aquarium trade (or at least there have been no reports or photos of living specimens yet). Aquarium conditions should be the same as for any of the other Surinam corys or for that matter the same as most other corys.

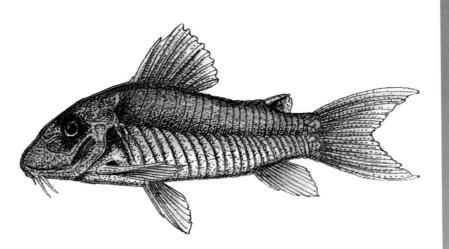

Corydoras flaveolus.

CORYDORAS FLAVEOLUS R. VON IHERING, 1911

The holotype is the only specimen known. It comes from the tributaries to Rio Piracicaba above Salto, Sao Paulo, Brazil. Virtually nothing is known about this species. The holotype has lost all color and the fins are in very poor shape. The size is 3.36 cm. For all anybody knows this species is being imported under another name. Until live specimens are captured it shall probably remain "incognito."

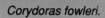

Corydoras fowleri.

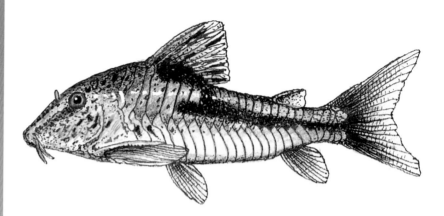

CORYDORAS FOWLERI BOEHLKE, 1950

The holotype, apparently a gravid female, was taken at Cano del Chancho near Pebas, Loreto, Peru. A second specimen was purchased in Leticia, Colombia. The species grows to about a length of 7 cm. The pattern is quite distinctive and should not be confused with any other species of *Corydoras*. Females are fuller in the mid-section and somewhat more compactly built than the males. A 20-gallon tank is recommended for this larger species. The water temperature should be about 21-24°C. This species is virtually never seen in the hobby.

Corydoras garbei. Photo by Dr. H. J. Franke.

CORYDORAS GARBEI
R. VON IHERING, 1911

C. garbei comes from the Rio Sao Francisco, Bahia, Brazil. It was collected by E. Garbe, after whom the species was named. Additional specimens were apparently available to Miranda-Ribeiro from Rio Granjeiro, Estado Ceara, Brazil, thereby extending its range. This species seems to be covered almost haphazardly with blotches. There is a dark band in the dorsal fin and the caudal fin has a series of bands on the fin membranes only (not the rays). Occasional individuals of this species appear in the hobby and seem to survive quite well in ordinary conditions recommended for other *Corydoras* species.

Corydoras geryi.
Photo by INPA.

CORYDORAS GERYI NIJSSEN & ISBRÜCKER, 1983

This species was named in honor of Dr. J. Gery. It comes from near the city of Trinidad, Rio Mamore basin, Beni Province, Bolivia. The color pattern is distinctive in that the body is quite plain (bluish to greenish) but the dorsal caudal, and adipose fin are banded with black. It is an average sized species of about 4 cm standard length. Few individuals are seen in the hobby, most likely because not many fishes are shipped out of Bolivia. It should be accommodated in situations that are comfortable for other species of *Corydoras*.

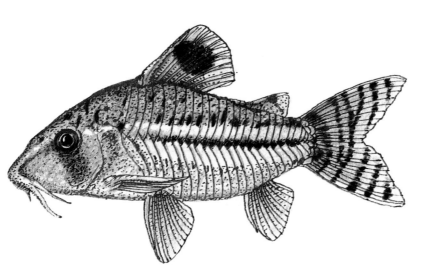

Corydoras gomezi.

CORYDORAS GOMEZI CASTRO, 1986

Described from Lakes of the Isla de Mocagua, Rio Amazonas/Solimoes near Leticia, Colombia, this 3.7-cm species closely resembles *Corydoras trilineatus* and *C. leopardus* but differs in details of the color pattern, including the black blotch in the dorsal fin of *C. gomezi* being medial in position, not terminal (i.e., there is a clear area above the spot). From the very similar *C. orphnopterus* it differs mostly in proportions, but the black mark in the adipose fin of *C. gomezi* is absent in *C. orphnopterus*.

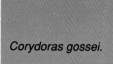

Corydoras gossei.

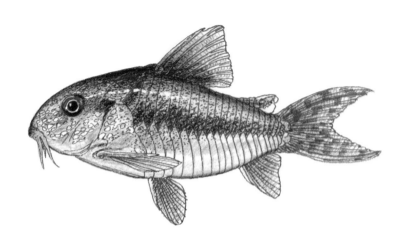

CORYDORAS GOSSEI NIJSSEN, 1971 (1972)

C. gossei was discovered in a creek near Guajara Mirim, Rio Mamore system, state of Rondonia, Brazil. This is a plain bodied species that in many ways resembles *C. aeneus.* However, its head is spotted with a lighter color and the caudal fin is banded. It differs also from *C. aeneus* in certain proportional measurements according to Nijssen. Apparently it is not available in the hobby and nothing is known about the requirements for this species. It should. however, accept the same condition as other corys without complaint. It was named in honor of Dr. J. P. Gosse, who collected the first specimens. In the original description this species was compared only with *C. aeneus* on the basis of color pattern. Aquarists are familiar enough with *C. aeneus* so that these two should not be confused.

Corydoras gracilis.
Photo by H. Bleher.

CORYDORAS GRACILIS NIJSSEN & ISBRÜCKER, 1976

This diminutive species was described on the basis of three specimens collected from the Rio Madeira within 100 miles of Porto Velho, Brazil, and three from a tributary of Rio Tapajos, 66.5 km west of Itaituba, Estado Para, Brazil. The largest specimen, the holotype, was only 23.2 mm standard length. It differs from all other *Corydoras* species by color pattern.

The most distinctive character is a dark brown band that runs from the mouth, through the eye, along the upper portion of the body paralleling the back, to the upper caudal base and then onto the caudal fin at an angle to end at about the tip of the middle rays. Obviously, such a small species is best kept in a single species tank that is well planted. No particular conditions are known for this fish, which is virtually never seen in the hobby.

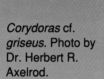

Corydoras cf. *griseus.* Photo by Dr. Herbert R. Axelrod.

CORYDORAS GRISEUS HOLLY, 1940

C. griseus was originally recorded as being from small side streams in the vicinity of the Amazon River, Brazil. Obviously, this was inadequate when one considers the extent of the Amazon. The type locality was later restricted by Nijssen & Isbrücker to the Kuribong Trail, Potaro River, Essequibo, Guyana, because the holotype was lost in WWII and the Brazilian locality was given for an aquarium specimen and very unreliable. The maximum size is 5 cm. The name *griseus* means gray, and this not very attractive species has not become popular with aquarists. With few individuals in captivity it apparently has not yet been spawned. As for aquarium conditions this fish conforms to the requirements of other cory species.

Corydoras guapore. Photo by Dr. H. J. Franke.

CORYDORAS GUAPORE KNAACK, 1961

Harald Schultz collected the first specimens from the main stream of the upper Rio Guapore, Rondonia, Brazil. In the aquarium, this species has been described as an active, nimble species that constantly is on the search for food. Because of this swimming activity (which is also seen in the dwarf armored catfishes *C. hastatus* and *C. pygmaeus*) greater open spaces and a water current (perhaps provided by a powerful filter) should be offered. In a well-planted 15- to 20-gallon tank, the pH should be about 6.5-7.2, the hardness 5-18°dGH, and the temperature range 21-24°C. Under certain conditions (proper temperature) this species may be suitable for a community tank. *C. guapore* attains a length of about 5 cm. Feeding is no problem as it will accept almost any suitable foods, even tablet, flake, frozen and freeze-dried foods. It prefers live foods such as mosquito larvae, *Daphnia* and enchytrae. The blotch on the caudal peduncle reminds one of *C. caudimaculatus*, but that species is much more spotted and has a larger blotch. *C. panda*, another species with a peduncular blotch (spot), has a black dorsal fin. No spawning reports are currently available.

Corydoras guianensis.

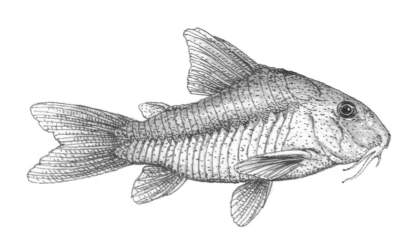

CORYDORAS GUIANENSIS NIJSSEN, 1970

As the name implies, this species is from the Guianas, more precisely, from the Nickerie, Coppename, and Saramacca River systems in Surinam, and may be expected to be found in adjacent waters. The largest specimens were only about 4 cm standard length. Little is known about this species as it does not appear in the hobby. Similar conditions for other cory species should suffice for this species as well.

CORYDORAS HABROSUS WEITZMAN, 1960

Dr. A. Fernandez-Yepez collected the original specimens from the Rio Salinas, a tributary of the Rio Pao Viejo, El Baul, Codajes, Venezuela. This diminutive species is only a little over 2 cm in standard length, with the females a little bit larger than the males. The size and color pattern are enough to distinguish this species from all others. Water conditions are not critical though there should be 33% water changes every three to four days. The tank should be well planted, perhaps with some *Hygrophila polysperma* included. The recommended pH is 6.2, the best temperature 25°C. Chopped tubifex and whiteworms are preferred foods. Males are slightly

Corydoras habrosus. Photo by H. J. Richter.

Corydoras habrosus, juvenile with deformed eye. Photo by Alan Pinkerton.

smaller than the females and much slimmer. Spawning has been accomplished on one occasion and described as follows. The male follows the female about the tank as normal in prespawning cory courtship. He swims about the female touching her on the head and body with his body. Most contact appears to be with his barbels touching her head. Eventually the female accepts the male's advances and spawning commences. In most instances they assume the T-position. First of all there are some "practice" runs where no eggs are extruded. Then, there appears a single 2mm egg. This is carried by the female to a previously cleaned spot. Favored for egg deposition are small plants near the substrate, particularly on the underside of the leaves (rarely is one placed on top). It was observed that the spawning male "protected" the female from other males attempting to spawn with her. About 50 eggs were eventually counted. These were placed at different levels in the tank. Before and after the spawning the fish were fed

Corydoras habrosus, juvenile. Photo by Alan Pinkerton.

normally and seemed to take little or no interest in the eggs. By the morning of the 5th day the eggs had darkened considerably and were starting to hatch. The fry quickly disappeared into the gravel and plants. After 2-3 days microworms were fed twice a day and a 1/3 water change was made. The first two weeks was the critical period, when most losses occurred. After that the losses declined. Finely chopped tubifex and microworms were fed daily and every two days a 50% water change was made. At about 10 weeks the adult pattern was apparent but not clearly defined although it did become stronger in the next few weeks. In this case the spawning was decidedly seasonal as there was a spawning hiatus of about 6 months starting in November.

Corydoras haraldschultzi. Photo by Dr. H. J. Franke.

CORYDORAS HARALDSCHULTZI KNAACK, 1962

C. haraldschultzi comes from the Rio Tocantins, Rio Araguaia, and the upper Rio Guapore, a border river between Brazil and Bolivia. It was discovered by Harald Schultz and named in his honor. It is a peaceful, social species, happiest when living in groups. It can be kept for the most part as in other *Corydoras.* However, a larger tank of about 20-gallon capacity with strong filtration and nitrate-free water is necessary. It should be well planted. *C. haraldschultzi* also needs a great deal of free swimming room and some current. Peat-filtered water is advantageous. It eats everything, with dried food and tablet food happily taken, but live foods are preferred, particularly bottom-living insect larvae. The recommended temperature range is 24-28°C. Spawning is said to be seasonal, as in many cory species, with most activity occurring during the northern winter—December through March seem to be most productive months. The sexes are difficult to distinguish except by body shape when the females are ripe. For spawning soft, peat filtered water with a pH value around 6, and a hardness below 10°dGH should be used according to reports. Java fern should be added as a spawning substrate. The males should outnumber the females (for example 1-2 females and 3-5 males). Condition the spawners well with nourishing live food (mosquito larvae are very good) as well as nutritious frozen food. Prespawning activities are normal and when spawning itself occurs the usual T-position is seen. During each spawning bout 2-4 eggs are dropped by the female into her ventral fin pouch. These are then taken by

Corydoras haraldschultzi. Photo by Harald Schultz.

Corydoras haraldschultzi, juvenile. Photo by Alan Pinkerton.

the female and placed at a previously cleaned site where they adhere to the substrate. In about 3 1/2 hours only about 50 eggs were produced. Later spawnings produced larger batches of eggs with a maximum of 230. The eggs, 2 mm in diameter, are laid primarily on the underside of Java fern leaves in close proximity to each other. Hatching occurred in 4 days at 24°C. The second day after hatching microworms should be added. The fry are blotchy with a dark line running from the eye to the snout. After two weeks the fry should have grown to about 9 mm in length; after 3 more weeks they should attain a length of 15 mm, at which time they have a mask that the adults lack. At first the fry can be fed live food and powdered pellets; after 2 weeks finely chopped tubifex. Adults have a length of about 7 cm. *Corydoras haraldschultzi* is often confused with *C. sterbai* because of the similarity in color pattern, but *C. haraldschultzi* has a light colored face with dark spotting, whereas *C. sterbai* has a sooty face with pale spots.

Corydoras hastatus. Photo by Dr. H. J. Franke.

CORYDORAS HASTATUS EIGENMANN & EIGENMANN, 1888

C. hastatus occurs in the Amazon basin and southern Brazil (Mato Grosso, Descalvados, Villa Bella) and the Rio Paraguay near Corumba, Paraguay. It is one of the two smallest cory species (the other being C. cochui)

and differs from most other corys in being free swimming. One can see it in small schools remaining motionless in mid-water at times instead of scouring around the bottom like almost every other cory. It lives among plants, moving about like species of *Otocinclus*. Because of its small size and delicate nature it is best kept in a single species tank. The recommended water chemistry includes a pH of about 6.8 and a hardness of 4.5°dGH. Aquarists have successfully spawned this species in captivity but the extremely small size of the fry makes raising them quite difficult. Very small food (particularly infusoria) is required for prolonged periods. Despite its differences, *C. hastatus* spawns in typical cory fashion. However, only one, seldom two, 1.2 mm long eggs are produced per pairing, totaling 20-40 per female in a day. These are usually placed at the bottom sections of plants (such as *Myriophyllum*), on free-lying roots (never on their leaves), or even on the aquarium glass. At 26°C, the 5 mm long fry hatch out in 4 days. Rearing is best accomplished with living or frozen rotifers or with newly hatched *Artemia* nauplii. After three weeks the young are about 15 mm long and already exhibit the black longitudinal stripes. This species is often confused with *C. pygmaeus*, another dwarf species, but the color patterns differ. *C. hastatus* has a large black blotch at the tail base that is as deep as the caudal base and extends onto the tail. *C. pygmaeus* has a dark longitudinal line from the snout that is somewhat expanded on the tail base but not to the entire depth of the base.

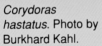

Corydoras hastatus. Photo by Burkhard Kahl.

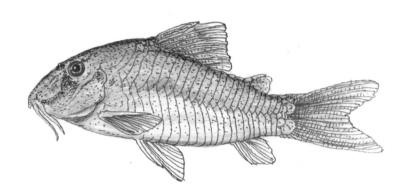

Corydoras heteromorphus.

CORYDORAS HETEROMORPHUS NIJSSEN 1970

This poorly known species comes from the Coppename and Saramacca River systems, Surinam. It attains a standard length of almost 5 cm. So far it has not been reported in the aquarium trade and nothing is known about its keeping and breeding. It should not differ significantly from the needs of most other corys, so similar conditions can be used.

Corydoras imitator.
Photo by Dr. H. J.
Franke.

CORYDORAS IMITATOR NIJSSEN & ISBRÜCKER, 1983

This is the long-snouted form of *C. adolfoi* from the upper Rio Negro (Sao Gabriel da Cachoeira). Adult females are larger and heavier than males. It is a peaceful schooling fish, so that at least six should be kept together. Since it may be just a larger variant of *C. adolfoü*, all conditions for that species apply to this one.

Corydoras imitator.
Photo by Dr. H. J.
Franke.

CORYDORAS JULII STEINDACHNER, 1906

This species was found in small tributaries in the lower Amazon around Belem, Brazil. It is a peaceful fish that happily schools with other armored catfishes. It is suggested that much more open swimming room be available at the bottom, which should be composed of fine sand. The 15- to 20-gallon tank should be sparsely planted with *Echinodorus* and *Vallisneria*. Fine-leaved plants such as *Cabomba* are also suitable. Few demands are placed on the water conditions. A pH of 6.5-7.8, a hardness of up to 20°dGH, and a temperature of 23-26°C are recommended. Regular partial water changes every 2-3 weeks are expedient. *C. julii* accepts a variety of items from dried and flake foods to live foods (daphnia and mosquito larvae), the latter of course always preferable. No spawning reports are available for the true *C. julii.* For a long time another species of *Corydoras, C. trilineatus,* went under this name. According to Nijssen the true *C. julii* is rarely imported. *C. julii* is often confused with *C. trilineatus,* which has a reticulated head pattern. In *C. julii* the head is spotted. Besides, *julii* is smaller and more compact. This species attains a length of about 5.5 cm.

Corydoras julii.

Corydoras lamberti.

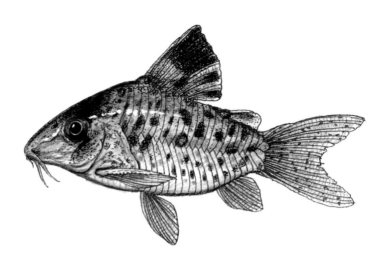

CORYDORAS LAMBERTI NIJSSEN & ISBRÜCKER, 1986

C. *lamberti* is known from only three specimens taken in the lower course of the Rio Huytoyacu, a right bank tributary to the Rio Pastaza, Peru. The largest of the three had a standard length of 3.8 cm. No comparisons were made in the original description but the illustration and a photo of the holotype are very reminiscent of C. *ambiacus*. C. *lamberti* has, however, a large black blotch in the upper-anterior part of the dorsal fin and the spots on the body are not as neatly arranged in horizontal lines. The caudal fin also has vertical rows of small dots rather than the heavier dotted lines of C. *ambiacus*. The species apparently is not in the aquarium hobby and no photos of living individuals are available. There should be no problem keeping this fish under the same conditions as one would keep other corys.

Corydoras latus from Humaita, Brazil. Photo by Dr. Herbert R. Axelrod.

CORYDORAS LATUS PEARSON, 1924

C. *latus* is one of the C. *aeneus* look-alikes. It was originally discovered in lagoons at Lago Rogoagua, Rio Beni basin, Rondonia, Brazil. It attains a standard length of about 4.2 cm. This species has undoubtedly been sold under the name of C. *aeneus* because of its close resemblance to that species. It is, however, deeper bodied and sports some vertical barring in its caudal fin. It may also be confused with the Venezuelan C. *concolor* but that species appears shorter and "chunkier" than C. *latus* and does not have the greenish sheen or the caudal fin barring of *latus*. C. *latus* can be kept under the same conditions as C. *aeneus* with no difficulty.

Corydoras leopardus. Photo by D. D. Sands.

CORYDORAS LEOPARDUS MYERS, 1933

C. leopardus was originally described from "Brazil, one of the coastal rivers south of the Amazon." This certainly was not sufficient and Nijssen and Isbrücker restricted the type locality to coastal waters around Maracana (north from Belem), Para, Brazil. *C. julii,* a very similar species with which it is often confused, occurs about 500 km west of this locality in the mouth of the Amazon area. *C. leopardus* is apparently a wide-ranging species since Nijssen and Isbrücker also record it from Peru and Ecuador. It is a peaceful, hardy, and lively species that would be suitable for the community tank as long as they are housed with similarly peaceful inhabitants. It is easily kept in a 15-gallon tank in groups of about 6-10 or more individuals. Water conditions are not very important; a pH of 6.5-7.5 and a hardness of up to 20°dGH are suitable, along with a temperature range of 22-25°C. When making water changes be sure that the water is chlorine-free. All types of foods are accepted but live foods are preferred. In other words it can be kept as other *Corydoras* species. There are no spawning reports available. However, the spawning behavior should not differ perceptibly from other corys. Since the species is seldom imported, there is unfortunately an insufficient number of individuals that can be spawned. This species attains a length of 7 cm. At first glance *C. leopardus, C. julii, C. trilineatus*, and *C. punctatus* all look very much alike. They all have a large black blotch in the dorsal fin, a barred caudal fin, and a horizontal stripe at the juncture of the dorsal and ventral lateral plates. *C. punctatus*, as the name implies, however, is heavily spotted over head and body and the lateral stripe and the caudal fin stripes are rather obscure. *C. trilineatus*, on the other hand, also as its name implies, has additional stripes above and below the central one, the three lines separated one from the other by clear spaces. Its head and body are also covered more with elongate spots or even worm-like lines rather than roundish spots. *C. julii* is very similar but its head and body are covered with roundish spots (larger and less numerous than those of *C. punctatus*). *C. leopardus* has the sinuous line-spots of *trilineatus* but lacks the additional two lines flanking the central horizontal body line. All these species are highly variable so that it would take a good deal of research and hundreds (or more) of specimens with accurate locality data to really define these species. Hopefully someone will undertake such a project and help clear things up.

Corydoras leucomelas. Photo by Dr. H. J. Franke.

CORYDORAS LEUCOMELAS EIGENMANN & ALLEN, 1942

This species was originally discovered in Yarinacocha, Peru, but apparently its range also includes portions of Ecuador and Colombia. It has a length of about 4.5 cm. This is an ideal community tank species and can be housed in a 15- to 20-gallon tank with small tetras, dwarf cichlids, and other peaceful species. The water should have a pH of about 6.2-7.2, a hardness to 12°dGH, and a temperature range of 22-26°C. The females are more rounded in the belly region and the males have more elongate and pointed pelvic fins. Unfortunately, there are no spawning reports available. According to Nijssen and Isbrücker the caudal base has a narrow, black vertical bar, followed by an unpigmented zone of twice the width, which is diagnostic for the species.

Corydoras loretoensis. Photo by D. D. Sands.

CORYDORAS LORETOENSIS NIJSSEN & ISBRÜCKER, 1986

This species comes from the Rio Nanay area of Loreto, Peru. It is a rather small species of 4 cm standard length. *C. loretoensis* is reminiscent of *C. armatus*, both with elongate dorsal fin spines, but among other things it is much less deep bodied than that species. *C. loretoensis* also has small grayish brown spots and dots scattered over the entire body, whereas in *C. armatus* they are more or less confined to the anterior portion of the body. This is a very social species and does best if at least six individuals are kept together in a 15-gallon or larger tank. The recommended temperature range is 22-25°C. Other conditions should be as for normal *Corydoras* aquaria.

Corydoras loxozonus. Photo by Aaron Norman.

CORYDORAS LOXOZONUS NIJSSEN & ISBRÜCKER, 1983

C. loxozonus comes from Meta, Lomalinda near Rio Ariari, Colombia. It is a very distinctive species that has a black bar at the anterior portion of the dorsal fin to the upper body and thence across the body toward the lower caudal peduncle and onto the lower portion of the caudal fin. This species when first introduced into the aquarium trade went under the name *Corydoras deckeri* but it was never described under that name. It is a peaceful, group-loving species that is suitable for the community tank of 15- to 20-gallon capacity. The temperature range should be a bit on the low side at 21-24°C. Small live foods are preferred but other aquarium fare is readily accepted. It should spawn in a manner similar to other corys. This fish attains a length of about 6 cm.

CORYDORAS MACROPTERUS REGAN, 1913

C. macropterus is one of those species that differ significantly from your run-of-the-mill *Corydoras* species. Like *C. barbatus* it comes from Brazil around Sao Paulo. Also like *C. barbatus,* males have better developed bristles which are affectionately known as "whiskers." The dorsal and pelvic fins of adult males are also substantially larger than in the females (*macropterus* means big fin). This is a peaceful, friendly species that should be kept in small aggregations. With a maximum size of 10 cm or thereabouts the tank should be larger than for most corys, perhaps a 30- to 50-gallon size is more suitable. When placed in a community tank fin-nibbling species (such as the tiger barbs) should be avoided. It is a bit sensitive to new conditions and often may be a problem to acclimatize. Once settled in, however, everything should go well. The pH is

Corydoras macropterus, male. Photo by Harald Schultz.

not critical and can be 6.5-7.5, the hardness up to 18°dGH. On the other hand the temperature must be kept on the low side, about 18-21°C, as this species becomes restless at higher temperatures, perhaps due to a lowering of the dissolved oxygen. Feeding is no problem although during the acclimatization period live foods should be offered. Later frozen and even dried foods can form part of the diet along with some vegetable matter. Because of the obvious differences between *C. barbatus* and *C. macropterus* and the rest of the species of *Corydoras* I would think that the genus *Scleromystax* (type species *C. barbatus*) should be resurrected for these two species.

Corydoras macropterus, male. Photo by Dr. H. J. Franke.

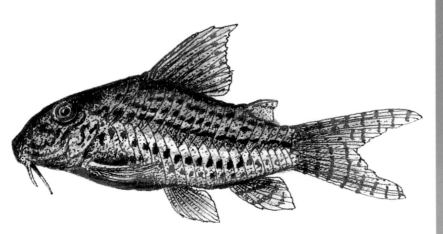

*Corydoras
maculifer.*

CORYDORAS MACULIFER NIJSSEN & ISBRÜCKER, 1971

C. *maculifer* comes from the Mato Grosso region of Brazil, around Rio das Mortes. It is a small species with a standard length of about 3.5 cm. It is not very well known but should do well under the same conditions as most *Corydoras* species. The pattern consists of horizontal spot-rows on the body and vertical stripes in the caudal fin (perhaps similar to the pattern of C. *leucomelas*), but there is no dorsal blotch or mask.

Corydoras melanistius brevirostris. Photo by Burkhard Kahl.

CORYDORAS MELANISTIUS BREVIROSTRIS FRASER-BRUNNER, 1947

This subspecies of *C. melanistius* comes from the Orinoco River in Venezuela. It is less shy than some corys and well suited for a community tank with fishes that are not aggressive feeders. A 15- to 20-gallon tank is recommended. It should be well planted and have a fine-grained dark substrate. The water conditions should include a pH of 6-7.8, a hardness of 25°dGH, and a temperature of 20-24°C. It accepts most foods commonly available for aquarium fishes. It attains a length of about 6 cm. *C. wotroi* is a synonym. *C. melanistius brevirostris* differs from *C. m. melanistius* by having fewer but larger body spots, 4-5 black spot-rows on the caudal, and the more pointed dorsal fin.

Corydoras melanistius melanistius. Photo by Dr. Herbert R. Axelrod.

CORYDORAS MELANISTIUS MELANISTIUS REGAN, 1912

This subspecies of *C. melanistius* comes from Essequibo, Guyana. It attains a length of about 6 cm. Its care is the same as the other subspecies, and it breeds in a manner typical for the genus. Teichner reported increased sensitivity to fungus and a high degree of shyness. His fish spawned after a complete water change at night (hardness 12-15°dGH). The turning on of the light prompted an immediate cessation of the spawning. There were 45 eggs, on average 1.7-1.8 mm in diameter, that were deposited individually, rarely by pairs. Of these only about one third hatched out. In later spawnings, when he broke the spawners up into two groups of 4 males and one female, in one group out of 18 eggs 9 hatched, while in the other group 13 young hatched out of 35 eggs. These were first fed with microworms and Grindal worms, and later with chopped tubifex. No problems were encountered.

Corydoras melanotaenia. Photo by H. J. Richter.

CORYDORAS MELANOTAENIA REGAN, 1912

The Rio Meta basin in Colombia is the home of this species. It is a peaceful species and suitable for a community tank. Normal water conditions should prevail: pH 6.5-7.2, hardness up to 17°dGH, and a temperature range of 23-25°C. Feeding is no problem with most aquarium type foods accepted. It should be kept in tank situations as in other *Corydoras* and spawns in a typical manner. The eggs are adhesive and are usually attached to the broad leaves of plants. The larvae hatch after 5 days and can be started with newly hatched brine shrimp. About 150-180 eggs are commonly deposited.

Corydoras melini.
Photo by Burkhard Kahl.

CORYDORAS MELINI LONNBERG & RENDAHL, 1930

This strikingly patterned *Corydoras* comes from the Rio Papuri, Rio Uaupes in the Brazilian state of Amazonas. It grows to a length of about 5 cm. The care and breeding of this species are typical for the genus. *C. melini* is most often confused with *C. metae* but differs from that species by having black only at the base of the dorsal fin (in *metae* the whole fin is usually black) and the black stripe extending onto the lower edge of the caudal fin (in *metae* it stops abruptly at the caudal fin base).

Corydoras metae, the form or species called *davidsandsi,* showing the dark stripe along the midback. *C. melini* is shown for comparison and has the midback golden. Photo by Dr. H. J. Franke.

CORYDORAS METAE EIGENMANN, 1914

The specific name of this *Corydoras* species comes from its origin, the Rio Meta in Colombia (more precisely from the vicinity of Barrigona). It attains a maximum size of about 6 cm. It is omnivorous, eating a variety of foods, but preferring live and/or frozen foods over the dried types as do most fishes. It is closely related to *C. melini* (the distinction in color pattern is given above) and *C. potaroensis* (completely different color pattern). The water conditions for keeping this species are the same as for most corys. A successful spawning took place in a tank where the pH was 7.0, the hardness was 13°dGH (of which 12° was KH), and a temperature between 21° and 23°C. The spawners were conditioned on frozen *Daphnia, Cyclops,* mosquito larvae, and tubifex. The activities began in the evening at about 1800 hours when two males began to drive and swim around the female frenetically. After

Corydoras metae. Photo by Dr. H. J. Franke.

the successful stimulation of a female the male ceases this frantic courtship and they begin actual spawning. The pair swim around each other until their movements culminate in a T-position with the male crosswise before the female and resting on the bottom. At this point there is usually a firm clasping of the female's barbels by the male but in this case it was not observed. During the delivery of the sexual products the partners bent toward one another and lay with the sides of their bodies approximately parallel to one another. These couplings last approximately 30 seconds, after which the female remains motionless on the bottom. When the female again begins to move, she searches for a place to deposit the eggs that she is holding in the basket formed by her pelvic fins. On average about every six

Corydoras metae juveniles. Photo by Dr. H. J. Franke.

minutes only one egg (total 15-36 overall) is attached to large-leaved water plants such as *Echinodorus osiris* and *Cryptocoryne beckettii.* Altogether the spawning lasted approximately 5 hours. These events occur several times in a 14-day rhythm. About 60% of the spawn fungused, and in later spawnings even more did. However, the hatch rate can be elevated by the addition of Trypaflavin (=Acriflavin). At 23°C the young hatched out after 7 days. After an additional 3 days the fry can be fed with mashed *Cyclops* nauplii, and later finely chopped tubifex can be added. By feeding tubifex the young seem to grow substantially faster. After eight weeks the young had attained a length of about 2 cm long.

Eberhardt, who also reported on the spawning of this species, distinctly recognized the customary T-position with the tight-clamping of the female's barbels by the pectoral fins of the male. The eggs were deposited on the side glass near the water surface (possibly as the result of lack of large-leaved plants) and in the thick Java moss at 5-15 minute intervals. Mostly only one, but sometimes 2 eggs are deposited. The entire spawning bout lasted about 8 hours. From a single female 86 eggs were deposited. At 23°-26°C 82 fry hatched out after 5 days. The young catfishes were fed with rotifers on the 4th day. After a week they had reached a length of 10 mm.

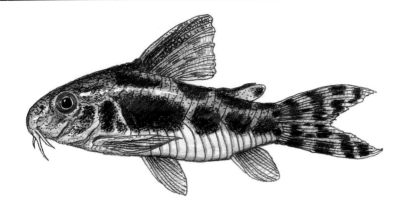

Corydoras micracanthus. (Artist's conception.)

CORYDORAS MICRACANTHUS REGAN, 1912

C. *micracanthus* was originally collected at Salta, Argentina, by Borelli (after whom the dwarf cichlid *Apistogramma borellii* was named). Very little is known about this 4 cm standard length species. The original description follows: "Depth of body 3 to 3½ in the length, length of head 4. Diameter of eye 6 or 7 in length of head; snout as long as postorbital part of head or interorbital width. Suborbital narrow; barbels nearly or quite reaching gill-opening. Dorsal I, 8; spine ½ the length of head; fin small, rounded, its base less than its distance from adipose fin, which is preceded by 1 or 2 median scutes. Anal I 6. Pectoral spine not reaching base of pelvic fin. Scutes 25/22; humeral shields widely separated below, each separated by 2 scutes from base of pelvic fin. Yellow, with a series of 3 to 6 dark brownish or purplish spots along the side and a second series on the back; dorsal dusky anteriorly, sometimes with spots on rays; caudal barred; lower fins immaculate."

It is assumed that normal aquarium conditions suitable for other *Corydoras* species will suffice for this species as well, but coming from Argentina it would be best to keep the temperatures on the cool side.

CORYDORAS MULTIMACULATUS STEINDACHNER, 1907

C. multimaculatus was collected and described by F. Steindachner from central and northern Brazil. Nijssen and Isbrücker later restricted the type locality to a tributary to the Rio Preto near Santa Rita de Cassia, Bahia, Brazil. Its maximum length is 6 cm. Although it is rarely seen in the aquarium trade it has been reported as a peaceful community tank fish. Like other corys it is omnivorous and an active bottom feeder. It can be kept under the same conditions as other *Corydoras* species. As the name implies it is a spotted species, those on the body appearing to be arranged in irregular horizontal rows. The head is covered with moderate sized spots and seems to lack a mask. All unpaired fins are provided with similar sized spots as those found on the body, those in the dorsal and caudal fins arranged in rows.

Corydoras nanus.
Photo by Burkhard Kahl.

CORYDORAS NANUS NIJSSEN & ISBRÜCKER, 1967

C. nanus occurs in the Suriname and Marowijne River systems, Surinam. It attains a length of about 4.5 cm standard length. It is commonly seen in the aquarium trade and does well under conditions that are adequate for other cory species. According to a spawning report by Matschke, about 10-15 eggs per pairing, of an average diameter of 1.2 mm, are deposited mostly on plant leaves. For the entire spawning as many as 600 eggs per female may be produced. At 26°C the fry hatch on the third day. The fry are very prone to illness during the early stages if they are not kept under optimal water and feeding conditions. At a size of approximately 2.5 cm they commonly swim free in the open middle layers of the tank as also do the adult animals. This very pretty catfish was for a long time erroneously called *C. undulatus*, a separate species. *C. nanus* is probably most closely related to *C. elegans* of the Amazon system near Cudajas, Brazil. *C. nanus*, however, does not have as deep a body as that species but a longer snout. *C. elegans* also has a main dark band in the upper part of its body, and less, more indistinct pattern below this. *C. nanus* has a basic pattern of three solid dark horizontal stripes on the body and an almost reticulated head and anterior back area. The dorsal fin may have two bands that break up into patches and spots.

Corydoras nanus.

Corydoras cf. *napoensis*. Photo by Burkhard Kahl.

CORYDORAS NAPOENSIS NIJSSEN & ISBRÜCKER, 1967

C. napoensis is another species that was named for its origin, a northern tributary to the Rio Aguarico, Napo, Ecuador. It is not restricted to Napo, however, and occurs also near Iquitos, Peru. It is a peaceful, schooling species that should be maintained in groups of at least six in 15- to 20-gallon tanks. Keeping and breeding conditions are similar to those for other *Corydoras* species. *C. napoensis* is somewhat similar to *C. nanus* from Surinam and in aquarium circles was even considered a color form of that species. Besides the geographic distinction, *C. napoensis* has more conspicuous unpigmented areas (in *nanus* they are ill-defined) and adult males have a large black blotch in the upper third or half of the dorsal fin (in *nanus* there is an irregular reticulate pattern which may coalesce into two bands). Males are more strongly patterned, while females are larger and have more girth. This species probably spawns like the sympatric *C. elegans*. It grows to a length of 5 cm.

Corydoras narcissus. Photo by Dr. Herbert R. Axelrod.

CORYDORAS NARCISSUS NIJSSEN & ISBRÜCKER, 1980

C. narcissus was collected by Axelrod, Bleher, Bossche, Gery, and Schwartz in a creek flowing into the Rio Ipixuna, Rio Purus system, Amazonas, Brazil. It appears to be the long-snouted version of the sympatric *C. arcuatus*. The patterns are the same, as are the keeping and breeding conditions. This species attains a standard length of about 6.5 cm.

Corydoras nattereri. Photo by Burkhard Kahl.

CORYDORAS NATTERERI STEINDACHNER, 1877

This old favorite of aquarists occurs from Rio de Janeiro to Rio Doce, including the Rio Paraiba and Rio Jequitinhonha, in southeastern Brazil. It attains a maximum length of 6-6.5 cm. Its care and breeding are as per the genus. However, it prefers lower temperatures (18-20°C) except during breeding. Temperatures in excess of 26°C seem to cause it some discomfort. Like other corys it is omnivorous, but should receive ample amounts of live foods (whiteworms, tubificid worms, *Daphnia*, etc.). According to Matschke about 30 eggs per female of an average 2 mm diameter are deposited on the plants or the side glass of the aquarium. At the lower temperature (23°C) that this species prefers, the fry hatch after 5 days. *C. nattereri* is very close to *C. prionotus* but differs by lacking a longitudinal series of small spots just below the anterior half of the midlateral stripe, by having smaller and less prominent spots on the dorsal and lateral parts of the head and snout, by having no ill-defined blotches below the base of the last dorsal fin ray and below the origin of the adipose fin spine, and by having smaller spots in dorsal and caudal fins.

Corydoras nijsseni.
Photo by H.
Mayland.

CORYDORAS NIJSSENI SANDS, 1989

The problem of minor differences in color pattern and/or snout shape among *Corydoras* specimens from a single locality is a major stumbling block in cory taxonomy. *Corydoras adolfoi*, for instance, occurs with a long-snouted type of fish with an identical pattern and a short-snouted type that differs in having the entire snout sooty, lacking a distinct band through the eye. The long-snouted form has been named *imitator*, and now the sooty-faced form has been officially described as *Corydoras nijsseni*. It seems hard to believe that three virtually identical species could co-exist, but only genetic and population studies will reveal the answer to the problem.

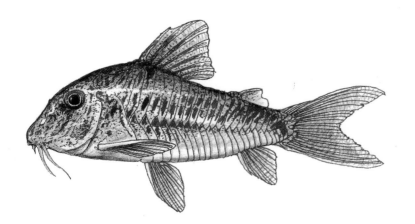

Corydoras octocirrus.

CORYDORAS OCTOCIRRUS NIJSSEN, 1970

C. octocirrus comes from Surinam (Surinam River system, Marowijne River system) and French Guiana (Marowijne River system). It was named *octocirrus* because of the presence of a third pair of rictal barbels; in other *Corydoras* species (except for *C. septentrionalis*) there are only two pairs of rictal barbels. Several species (long-snouted forms) have a triangular skin notch in the same place where the extra pair of barbels is formed in *octocirrus* and may be considered intermediate. *C. octocirrus* also has enlarged pectoral spines in adult males (but nothing to compare with those of *C. barbatus* and *C. macropterus*).

*Corydoras
oiapoquensis.*

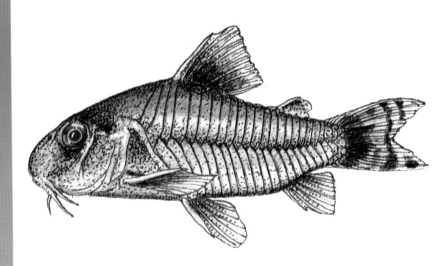

CORYDORAS OIAPOQUENSIS, NIJSSEN, 1972

The type locality, the Oyapok River, French Guiana, provided the name for this species. It attains a length of about 4 cm standard length. This is the short-snouted form associated with the sympatric long-snouted *C. condiscipulus*. Information given for that species also applies to this one.

Corydoras ornatus.
Photo by Dr.
Herbert R. Axelrod.

CORYDORAS ORNATUS NIJSSEN & ISBRÜCKER, 1976

This species occurs in tributaries to the Rio Tapajos, Brazil, where the pH is quite low (5.8) and the hardness is extremely low (2°dGH). However, in aquaria it is a bit more tolerant of the water conditions although it is very sensitive to higher concentrations of nitrites/ nitrates. Tanks of 15 to 20 gallons capacity with clear, well-filtered water with low hardness and a temperature range of 23-26°C are recommended. This is a peaceful, social species that does best when kept in small to larger groups. It reaches a length of 6 cm. Spawns have been reported although there is no specific data available. The three simple solid dark longitudinal lines on the body distinguish this species.

Corydoras orphnopterus. Photo by D. D. Sands.

CORYDORAS ORPHNOPTERUS WEITZMAN & NIJSSEN, 1970

   C. orphnopterus comes from the lower Rio Bobonaza, Pastaza River system, Ecuador. It is a peaceful species that is suitable for a community tank but not in association with fin-nibblers such as tiger barbs. A 15-gallon well-planted tank is sufficient for a group of about a half-dozen individuals (it should always be kept in groups). The substrate should be of a fine grain sand rather than any coarse-grained material with sharp angles. The water conditions should include a pH of 6.5-7.5, a hardness up to 20°dGH, and a temperature range of 20-24°C. Good filtration and a little current are also recommended. Mosquito and other insect larvae are best fed at first, especially to wild-caught individuals. Later prepared foods can be added to the diet. Spawning has not yet been reported. Females are paler, with finer spotting, and heavier. This species is most closely related to *C. ambiacus* but in *orphnopterus* the black in the dorsal fin is confined to the central part of the fin, whereas in *ambiacus* it is not only in the central part of the fin but extends to the black spot on the dorsal part of the body. *C. orphnopterus* reaches a length of 5.5 cm.

Corydoras osteocarus. Photo by Dr. Herbert R. Axelrod.

CORYDORAS OSTEOCARUS BÖHLKE, 1951

Dr. Carl Ternetz collected this species at San Fernando de Atabapo (where the Atabapo empties into the Rio Orinoco), Venezuela. It is also found in Surinam. Dr. Böhlke compared his species with *C. melanistius*, reporting that *C. osteocarus* is more elongate and less deeper bodied than that species. In color, *C. osteocarus* lacks the dark blotch or saddle, the barring of the caudal, the spot in the dorsal, and the dusky margin of the pectoral spine of *C. melanistius*. There are also fewer spots and fewer rows of spots on the sides of *osteocarus*. This peaceful species is quite sociable, preferring to be in groups. A well-planted 15- to 20-gallon tank is sufficient. The temperature range should be about 21-25°C. Females are larger and more heavy-bodied than the males. Spawning is accomplished in the typical T-position. Up to 300 eggs are spawned and usually attached to plants. At 21.4°C hatching occurs in approximately 3-4 days. The fry can be started with powdered food and chopped tubifex.

Corydoras ourastigma.

CORYDORAS OURASTIGMA NIJSSEN, 1972

Dr. J. P. Gosse collected the original specimens of this species from the Iquiri (=Rio Ituxi) about 47 kilometers from Rio Branco village, Rio Purus system, Estado Acre, Brazil. It attains a length of 6 cm in standard length. It is very close to *C. guapore* but differs in having a larger head, a longer snout, and a narrower interorbital than that species. *C. ourastigma* differs from the spot-tailed species by its smaller and more elongate oval peduncular spot. *C. panda* also has a black dorsal fin and no body spots while *C. guapore* has body spots. *C. caudimaculatus* has a more blunt snout and comes from the Rio Guapore system (as does *C. guapore*). Normal aquarium conditions may be implemented for this species and although no spawning reports are available it is expected to follow the same procedures as the majority of other *Corydoras* species.

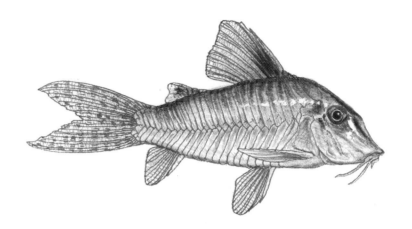

Corydoras oxyrhynchus.

CORYDORAS OXYRHYNCHUS NIJSSEN & ISBRÜCKER, 1967

C. oxyrhynchus was originally described from Gojo Creek, a tributary of the Saramacca River, Surinam. It attains a length of approximately 5 cm in standard length. According to Nijssen and Isbrücker it is apparently closest to *C. cervinus* of the upper Rio Guapore, Brazil. Besides the obvious locality difference, *C. oxyrhynchus* has a deeper body, longer pectoral spines, and a larger head. The color was described from preserved specimens. There were pepper-like gray spots covering the head, body, and fins (darker dorsally) and about ten irregular vertical bars on the caudal fin. No aquarium information is available on this species but it is expected that conditions suitable for most cory species will also be suitable for this one. It is expected to spawn in a similar manner as well.

Corydoras paleatus. Photo by Burkhard Kahl.

CORYDORAS PALEATUS (JENYNS, 1842)

This species is one of the most common and well-known of all the *Corydoras* species in the trade and one of the most easily kept and bred. It may even be the first one spawned as reports of success with this species go back as far as 1893. Many of the aquarium specimens are domestically bred rather than imported from the wild. It ranges from southeastern Brazil to northern Argentina and is reported to be quite abundant in the Rio de la Plata, as well as the Brazilian states of Rio Grande do Sul and Santa Caterina. It attains a maximum size of about 7.5 cm. It can be kept in a 15- to 20-gallon tank that is well planted and has average water conditions. The recommended temperature range for keeping this species is 18-20°C, but it should be higher (22-26°C) for spawning. It is omnivorous, but prefers live foods. This is one of the most prolific species. The rearing and spawning are

Corydoras paleatus. Photo by Dr. H. Grier.

unproblematical. The sexes are difficult to distinguish. Males are somewhat smaller and slimmer than the females, and their pectoral fins are a bit more pointed. Spawning is typical of the genus with a T-position assumed and the female cradling up to about 5 eggs in her pelvic fin basket. According to Knaack the females can produce, depending upon size, anywhere from 250 to 400 eggs. A domestically bred albinistic form is available, but this is less productive and somewhat more difficult to breed.

Corydoras paleatus. Photo by R. Zukal.

Corydoras panda variety. Photo by Dr. H. J. Franke.

CORYDORAS PANDA NIJSSEN & ISBRÜCKER, 1971

C. panda appears to be restricted to the Pachitea system. Specific localities are Aquas Amarillas, a tributary of the Rio Pachitea in the Departamento Huanuco, and Sira-mountain on the Rio Pachitea, which itself is a tributary of the Rio Ucayali, in the Departamento Coronel Portillo in Peru. This is a very peaceful species, suitable for relatively small tanks with small tetras or dwarf cichlids. It is a small species, with a length of about 4.5 cm, that can almost be counted among

Corydoras panda.
Photo by Dr.
Herbert R. Axelrod.

the dwarf armored catfish. Even so, the tank should be about 15 to 20 gallons capacity. They need good filtration, oxygen rich water, water changes every 3-4 weeks, and a temperature of 20-25°C. In nature they feed primarily on aufwuchs and small worms. Foersch and Hanrieder succeeded in collecting some specimens of this species in a narrow clearwater intake to the Rio Llulapichis in the Sira–mountain, which empties into the Rio Pachitea. The bottom was generally rocky, with no muddy areas or water plants present. The water conditions at the collecting site were a hardness of 7.7°dGH, of which 3.1°KH, and a temperature of only 22.2°C. Unfortunately, only two animals survived the trip back but these turned out to be a pair that were eventually spawned by Hanrieder. Foersch was able to breed some of the progeny and distributed them around to various aquarists. *C. panda* was spawned in a 10-gallon (30-liter) aquarium with a hardness of 16°dGH (13°KH) and a temperature range of 22-26°C. They were placed in the

Corydoras panda eating tubifex worms from a worm feeder. Photo by Dr. Herbert R. Axelrod.

spawning aquarium in groups with a ratio of 2,2 or 1,2 fish, although not all the pairs were willing to spawn. If they are conditioned with live or frozen *Daphnia* and perhaps tubificid worms for variety, the adults can spawn 10 to 14 times over a five-month period. After a normal spawning the eggs, occasionally several per mating bout, are placed on the glass near the water surface. They also were deposited near the bottom or in the Java moss. The eggs are approximately 1 mm in diameter and light yellow in color. The total number of eggs was not very great, maximally 40-60, and often fewer than 20. The higher numbers may have been the result of two or more females spawning simultaneously. Hatching occurred after 4 to 5 days. The survival rate was not great, leading one to think that something was not to the spawners' satisfaction. Raising the young was most successful with newly hatched brine shrimp and Grindal worms. The fry were about 2 cm long after 3 weeks. Foersch considers mulm removal simultaneously with the addition of fresh water as very important. The name *panda* was of course used because of the pattern resembling the Chinese panda that is so popular. The black dorsal and caudal peduncle spot are distinctive.

Corydoras pastazensis. Photo by Dr. Herbert R. Axelrod.

CORYDORAS PASTAZENSIS WEITZMAN, 1963

C. pastazensis was originally described on the basis of three specimens collected near the mouth of the Rio Bobonaza, a tributary to the Rio Pastaza, Ecuador. It was also later found in the Rio Ucayali system, Peru. It attains a length of up to 6.4 cm standard length. This is a hardy, peaceful species that is suitable for community tanks of slightly cooler water (20°-24°C) fishes. At least a 20-gallon tank should be provided. Clear soft water is preferred, and for water changes peat filtered water should be used. A large plant, perhaps an *Echinodorus* species in a pot, makes a suitable spawning substrate. Females are larger and have a rounder belly. Spawning proceeds as per normal cory spawning behavior. The color pattern of *C. pastazensis* is fairly distinctive. For the most part there is a broad diagonal band extending from the dorsal fin origin to the pelvic fins. The body behind this is quite variable depending upon locality, with few to many small spots to a couple of larger spots posteriorly in a line. The caudal fin is barred. A subspecies called *C. pastazensis orcesi* was described as having a convex posterior edge to the body bar and two spots on the posterior body below the adipose fin.

Corydoras polystictus, from Alto Juruena, Mato Grosso. Photo by Harald Schultz.

CORYDORAS POLYSTICTUS REGAN, 1912

C. *polystictus* comes from the tributaries of the eastern Rio Guapore (Mato Grosso, Brazil). It is a peaceful, social species that does best in a group of 5 to 8 animals. This small (to about 4 cm) species is well suited to community tanks that are populated only with delicate tetras and small non-aggressive cichlids. It can be well planted as plants are not molested although in searching for food in the substrate roots may be exposed. The tank size should be about 15 to 20 gallons. A good efficient filter that provides a strong current because of the oxygen requirements of this species is recommended. The bottom substrate should be of fine sand.The water conditions should include a pH of 6.2-7.5, a hardness of 18°dGH, and a temperature of 22-28°C. The species is somewhat nitrate sensitive so that frequent water changes, about every 3-4 weeks 1/3 of the tank capacity, should be made and frequent monitoring of the water conditions must be done. The spawning tank should be shallow (about 20 cm depth) and quite large. Several males

Corydoras polystictus. Photo by Dr. H. J. Franke.

should be added to a few females. Females are somewhat fuller and have a somewhat broader white section in the belly region. Feed the spawners normally. They will spawn in the same fashion as most other corys. As the name implies, this species is spotted, particularly anteriorly, with unmarked fins. Most of the other spotted species have at least a mask or banded caudal fin.

Corydoras potaroensis.

CORYDORAS POTAROENSIS MYERS, 1927

It was Carl Eigenmann himself who collected the original specimens of this species at Demerara, in the Potaro, a stream below Potaro Landing in the Essequibo system, Guyana. It attains a length of only about 4 cm standard length. This is a tan fish in which the posterior edges of the scutes are edged in black except anteriorly on the belly and above the pelvic fins. There is a well-developed dark mask. The fins are clear except the caudal fin has about 4 narrow dusky vertical bands at its base and the dorsal fin has an intense dark blotch. Weitzman compared *C. potaroensis* with *C. griseus*. The two species differ mostly in the eye size, that of *C. griseus* proportionately larger than that for *C. potaroensis*. Weitzman raised the question as to whether these might only be geographical variants. This species is not commonly imported for the aquarium trade but is expected to conform to the normal habits of most corys and their environment can be set up accordingly.

Corydoras prionotus.

CORYDORAS PRIONOTUS NIJSSEN & ISBRÜCKER, 1980

This look-alike of *C. nattereri* comes from the same area as that species, specifically southeastern Brazil. It grows to a length of about 5.3 cm standard length. The comparisons with *C. nattereri* were discussed under that species. Aquarium conditions and breeding habits should also be similar to those for *C. nattereri*, a better known species.

Corydoras pulcher.

CORYDORAS PULCHER ISBRÜCKER & NIJSSEN, 1973

The name *pulcher* means "pretty," and, indeed, this is a very attractive species. It was discovered north of Labrea in the Rio Purus, Rio Amazonas system, Estado Amazonas, Brazil. It attains a length of about 4.5 cm. To accommodate this species a 10- to 15-gallon tank should be set up with clear, well filtered water that is soft, slightly acid (peat-filtered to give it a slightly brownish tint), with a temperature range of 21-24°C. The sexes are hard to distinguish, the males being a bit smaller and more slender. Spawning should follow normal patterns. *C. pulcher* is very similar to *C. ornatus*, having basically four horizontal body stripes and a banded caudal fin. The bottom stripe in *C. pulcher*, however, extends along the lower portion of the body and actually along the base of the anal fin; this same stripe in *C. ornatus* rides higher on the body, touching the anal fin only at the last ray.

CORYDORAS PYGMAEUS KNAACK, 1966

This diminutive cory inhabits the environs of Calama at the mouth of the Rio Jiparana or Machado in the Rio Madeira, Brazil, Loreto, Peru, and the Rio Aguarico system in Ecuador. Females attain a length of about 3.5 cm, males are a bit smaller. *C. pygmaeus* is a peaceful, active, unpretentious, lovable, and easy to to breed catfish. It is quite a social species and should only be kept in groups, never singly. Because of its small size it, as also *C. hastatus*, should only be kept with similar small fish species, such as neon tetras, *Hyphessobrycon georgettae,* or the dwarf rasboras *Rasbora urophthalma* and *R. maculata. C. pygmaeus* is

Corydoras pygmaeus. Photo by H. J. Richter.

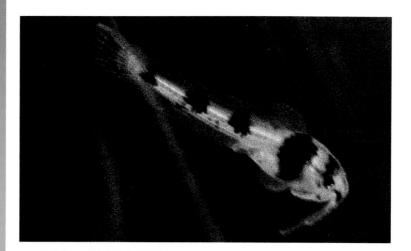

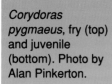

Corydoras pygmaeus, fry (top) and juvenile (bottom). Photo by Alan Pinkerton.

very similar to *C. hastatus* not only with regard to the small size, coloration, and habits, but also in spawning methods. It can be spawned in a 15-gallon tank heavily planted with species as *Hygrophila polysperma*. Conditioning can be accomplished primarily with whiteworms and tubifex, starting with 6 small feedings a day, reduced then to 3 later. A weekly water change of 25% is also recommended. Spawning proceeds normally, with the T-position assumed and usually a single egg extruded. Both *C. pygmaeus* and *C. hastatus* attach about 18-20 eggs, usually one by one and in no particular pattern, to aquarium plants or to the aquarium glass. They are opaque and about 2 mm in diameter. One interesting aspect of the reported spawning procedure is that the male protected the female from other males by positioning his body between the other males and the female. Every so often the female would rest. The eggs continue to darken as the embryos develop until the fry hatch out in three days at a temperature of 24°C (with higher temperatures this time is reduced — one claim is that the eggs hatched overnight!) and grow quite fast on a nourishing diet of Grindal worms, microworms, newly hatched brine shrimp, and various fry foods, and later with the addition of chopped tubifex. Feeding is done twice a day, which necessitates a one-third water change every three days. After 8 weeks they are already 20 mm long. The fry were differently colored from the adults. Adults and fry lived in harmony. Nieuwenhuizen reported that the spawning period extends from October to April. Knaack (1966) reported that this species should have been classified with the genus *Aspidoras*. In fact, examination of his *C. pygmaeus* material led him to announce that the genus *Aspidoras* should be regarded as a synonym for *Corydoras*. The comparison with *C. hastatus* appears under that species.

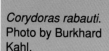
Corydoras rabauti. Photo by Burkhard Kahl.

CORYDORAS RABAUTI LAMONTE, 1941

   C. rabauti was described from seven preserved and three live specimens. It occurs in the Rio Yavari (Javari) in the Rio Ucayali system at the border of Peru with Brazil near Benjamin Constant, and Loreto, Peru. La Monte writes that she has bred specimens about 18 mm long, resulting in young that did not grow larger than 20 mm (Hoedeman). It attains a maximum size of about 6 cm. This species should be kept in groups in 15- to 20-gallon tanks in soft, slightly acid water. During spawning the males drive the females very strongly. This ends often in coupling in the T-position, at which time eggs and sperm are released. The female, with eggs in her pelvic fin basket and commonly followed by males, searches the environs for a place to place the eggs. One spot that seemed to be favored was the Java moss, into which the female swam. At that time at least one, sometimes two, eggs were deposited. By opening her fin basket in the midst of the plants the eggs are released and, being sticky, adhere to the leaves.The female may even remain for a time in the thickest part of the plant in order to avoid further advances by the pursuing males. Some of the eggs are sometimes stuck onto the bottom glass of the aquarium. This occurs when the female, in her struggles to get into the plant thicket, prematurely

Corydoras rabauti. Photo by Dr. H. Grier.

opens her fin basket and the eggs become lost. Very few eggs are found adhering to the side panes of the aquarium. After pairing, the female rests for a while on the bottom, then the males become active in courtship again and the female also becomes activated. At a temperature of 27°C the fry hatch out on the 4th day. As usual, the greatest fatalities occur in the early stages. About 70 to 80 eggs are deposited by each female. There are considerably fewer and larger eggs produced by C. rabauti than by C. zygatus. The fry are initially fed with small live foods, such as rotifers, which the young can take at the bottom. Later live or frozen *Cyclops* nauplii and chopped tubifex may be added. After 3 months they were on average 3 cm long. It is interesting that C. zygatus, a species from the upper Rio Huallaga near Tingo Maria in Peru, is colored almost exactly like C. rabauti and difficult to distinguish from it. C. zygatus is slightly more elongate, and the fins are a bit more transparent. Both of these characters are, however, only obvious when one can make a direct comparison of both species. The longitudinal band of C. rabauti also does not extend to the edge of the nape, while that of C. zygatus continues across the nape and connects up with the one from the opposite side. The caudal fin of C. zygatus is virtually clear, in C. rabauti the body bar crosses the caudal peduncle to extend onto the lower portion of the caudal fin. Whether this holds true on all individuals of both species, however, needs corroboration. For infallible characters that can readily distinguish the two species one must look to the juvenile coloration. In C. rabauti the fry and early juveniles, at least through the first month, have a wide dark vertical bar crossing the body just behind the head in contrast to C. zygatus, which has a spotted pattern at that size. A more exact comparison of the young forms of both C. zygatus and C. rabauti shows that 6-day-old C.

Corydoras rabauti.
Photo by R. Zukal.

rabauti are tri-colored, with the head strongly orange-colored, the anterior body inclusive of the lower half of the dorsal fin deep black, and the posterior portion of the body including the caudal peduncle ivory white. At the same age young *C. zygatus* were overall light tan or sand-colored with fine dark spotting. After about one month the head and all fins of young *C. rabauti* are a strong red-brown, the middle of the body a deep sea green, and the caudal peduncle an iridescent turquoise color.

The dark eye mask of the adult fish is visible at this time. Young *C. zygatus* are at this age sand-colored with a dark row of spots in the middle of the body. The sea green body coloration of the young *C. rabauti* first appears between the 3rd and 4th months. Even at this age, the characteristic dark longitudinal band slowly appears. Young *C. zygatus* have at the same age the coloration of the adult animals. In the trade *C. zygatus* is erroneously called *C. myersi*, which, however, is a synonym of *C. rabauti.*

Corydoras reticulatus. Photo by H. J. Richter.

CORYDORAS RETICULATUS FRASER-BRUNNER, 1938

Known localities for this species are the Amazon basin near Monte Alegre, Estado Para, Brazil, and Rio Ampiyacu, Loreto, Peru, the former the type locality. It attains a maximum length of about 5.5 cm. Under normal conditions for most cory species *C. reticulatus* breeds regularly in captivity. Similar to *C. sodalis*, it differs by having a black blotch or similar marking in the dorsal fin. In *C. sodalis* the dorsal fin may be banded but has no blotch. The body markings in *C. reticulatus*, as the name implies, are more reticulate.

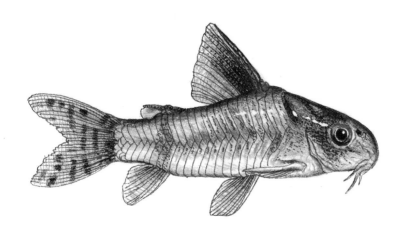

Corydoras reynoldsi.

CORYDORAS REYNOLDSI MYERS & WEITZMAN, 1960

C. reynoldsi was collected in a small caño off the Rio Orteguaza, Caqueta Province, Colombia. The caño had a sandy bottom, narrow sandy riffles, and deep (to 5 feet deep and 50 feet wide) holes. It was partly shaded by forest. The fish were actually taken in the sandy shallows where there was little current. A well-planted 15- to 20-gallon tank is sufficient with the water conditions within the normal range for corys. There are no spawning reports as yet for this species but it is expected to spawn in a manner similar to other *Corydoras* species. This species differs from all other corys in color pattern. There are two vertically elongate dark blotches or bars on the body, the first between the dorsal and pelvic fins, the second between the adipose and anal fins. The anterior dorsal fin and immediate base are dark and the caudal fin has 4 or 5 irregular cross-bars. This round-snouted species was compared to *C. melanistius* by the describers on the basis of its morphology, not of course the color pattern which is very different.

Corydoras robinae.
Photo by Dr.
Herbert R. Axelrod.

CORYDORAS ROBINAE BURGESS, 1983

This rather distinctive species of *Corydoras* was named for Robina Schwartz. It comes from the upper Rio Negro entry region (Rio Aiuana). It is quite peaceful and sociable, as are almost all small corys. A group will do well in a 15- to 20-gallon tank that is well planted and with water that has a pH of 5.6-7.0, hardness to 10°dGH, and a temperature range of 23-26°C. Small live foods such as worms and mosquito larvae may be needed as a starting diet. Until now there are no spawning reports. It is suggested that because of their origin peat-filtered soft water might be most beneficial. *C. robinae* attains a length of about 4 cm. One glance at the caudal fin of this fish should be enough to enable anyone to identify it once it is recognized as not being *Dianema urostriatum,* which has a similarly banded caudal fin.

CORYDORAS ROBUSTUS NIJSSEN & ISBRÜCKER, 1980

C. robustus was discovered in a creek less than one meter deep that runs into the Rio Ipixuna of the Purus system, Estado Amazonas, Brazil, by Axelrod, Schwartz, Gery, van den Bossche, and Bleher. It attains a total length of almost 10 cm, making it one of the larger species of *Corydoras*. According to the describers this species is apparently related to *C. ambiacus*. It is easily recognized, however, by its partially black dorsal fin, the color extending along the top of the back, and the black edging along the lower part of the caudal fin. The snout is pointed. It is rarely seen in the aquarium trade and little information on keeping and breeding is available. By its size, it should be afforded larger quarters than other, smaller corys, but the water conditions should be about the same.

Corydoras robustus. Photo by Dr. Herbert R. Axelrod.

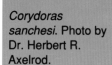

Corydoras sanchesi. Photo by Dr. Herbert R. Axelrod.

CORYDORAS SANCHESI NIJSSEN & ISBRÜCKER, 1967

According to Nijssen, *C. sanchesi,* from the Saramacca River system, Surinam, is closely related to and possibly even a subspecies of *C. osteocarus.* The only difference apparently is in the color pattern, *C. sanchesi* having (in some specimens) minute dots on head, body, and fins. The interorbital region, dorsal spine, and first soft dorsal fin ray (which is often prolonged) are dusky. This species is not often seen in the aquarium hobby and little information is available on its keeping and breeding. However, normal conditions for any cory should be acceptable. Up to 4 cm standard length.

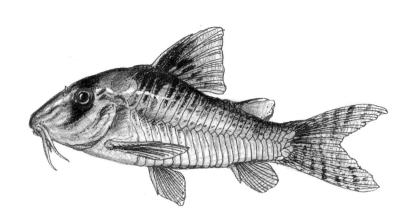

Corydoras saramaccensis.

CORYDORAS SARAMACCENSIS NIJSSEN, 1970

C. saramaccensis was named for the river where it was discovered, the Saramacca River, Brokopondo district, Surinam. It reaches 5.1 cm in standard length. According to Nijssen it is very close to *C. oxyrhynchus* but differing from that species in head structure, especially the shape of the snout. There is a dark band between the eyes and a dark blotch at the base of the anterior part of the dorsal fin. Vertical rows of gray spots are seen in the dorsal portion of the body running parallel to the scute edges. The caudal fin is crossed by 8 to 9 vertical bars. Aquarium care is similar to that of other species of *Corydoras*.

Corydoras schwartzi. Photo by Burkhard Kahl.

CORYDORAS SCHWARTZI RÖSSEL, 1963

This species was discovered near the mouth of the Rio Purus in Brazil. It reaches a maximum size of 4.5 cm. Conditions for keeping this cory are the same as for most other species of the genus although *C. schwartzi* is more warmth-loving. It differs from *C. surinamensis* (which was originally described as a subspecies of *C. schwartzi*) as described under that species as well as on a geographic basis.

Corydoras semiaquilus. Photo by Dr. Herbert R. Axelrod.

CORYDORAS SEMIAQUILUS WEITZMAN, 1964

This species was collected by Harald Schultz at Igarape Preto, a small jungle rivulet at the headwaters of the black water creeks that empty into the Rio Solimoes, Amazonas, Brazil. At the collecting locality the water was crystal clear, while the sandy bottom was covered with pebbles, leaves, and rotten leaves. It also was collected by Sven Kullander in the Rio Ucayali system, Loreto, Peru. It grows to a length of 6 cm in standard length. *C. semiaquilus* is close to *C. treitlii* in general aspect and color pattern but has barring in the dorsal, anal, and caudal fins. In *C. treitlii* these fins are unpatterned. Aquarium conditions should be similar to that for other species of *Corydoras*.

Corydoras semiaquilus, Rio Peixe Boi. Photo by Dr. Herbert R. Axelrod.

Corydoras cf. *septentrionalis*. Photo by Aaron Norman.

CORYDORAS SEPTENTRIONALIS GOSLINE, 1940

This Venezuelan species occurs in the Rio Pina (Rio Guarapiche system) and Rio Guanipa system. It is a current loving species from spring water and for that reason should be kept in a single species tank of about 15- to 20-gallon capacity where its special requirements can be met. For those who must keep it in a community tank it can only be kept with fishes from mountain creeks of the cooler tropical zone. The substrate should be of dark sand or crushed lava stone. Suggested water conditions include a pH of 6.0-7.5, a hardness of up to 18°dGH, and a temperature range of 20-23°C. It eats everything, so there is no problem with its diet as long as it is varied and nutritious. *C. septentrionalis* attains a length of 5.5 cm. This species was distinguished from *C. ellisae* on minor differences in proportions and spinules on the pectoral spines. The major difference seems to be in geography, *septentrionalis* coming from Venezuela, *ellisae* from Paraguay.

Corydoras simulatus. Photo by H. J. Richter.

CORYDORAS SIMULATUS WEITZMAN & NIJSSEN, 1970

C. simulatus comes from the Rio Meta system, Colombia. It is a peaceful species suitable for a community tank with good water conditions. Since it prefers clean, clear water with a current, a good filtration system with frequent changing of the filter material (every 4-6 weeks), and periodic water changes are recommended. In a 15- to 20-gallon aquarium the water should have a pH of 6.2-7.5, a hardness of up to 20°dGH, and a temperature range of 20-25°C. The substrate should be of coarse sand.

Planting can be accomplished according to your pleasure. The diet should include live foods but almost any aquarium foods are acceptable. This species grows to a length of 5.5 cm. *C. simulatus* resembles the "skunk" corys *C. melini* and *C. metae* in color pattern but has a distinctly longer snout. The name *simulatus* in fact refers to the similarity to *C. metae*. It resembles the long-snouted *C. septentrionalis* but differs in having a black base to the dorsal fin that *septentrionalis* lacks and *septentrionalis* has a large black midside body blotch; in *simulatus* it is present but weak.

Corydoras sodalis.
Photo by Burkhard
Kahl.

CORYDORAS SODALIS NIJSSEN & ISBRÜCKER, 1986

This species was described from the Rio Yavari, Loreto, Peru, and Rio Solimoes at Benjamin Constant, Brazil (at the border with Peru). It is peaceful and sociable, easily kept in a 15- to 20-gallon tank. Along with normal water chemistry, a temperature range of 22-26°C has been recommended. *C. sodalis* is a variable species that sometimes has solid, irregular lines on its upper body; at other times it has widely scattered small dots and spots. With the solid lines it resembles *C. reticulatus* but it can be distinguished from that species by its having dark bands in the dorsal fin whereas *C. reticulatus* has a large blotch, albeit irregular. *C. sodalis* attains a length of 5 cm.

Corydoras sodalis.
Photo by Andre
Roth.

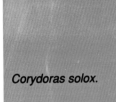

Corydoras solox.

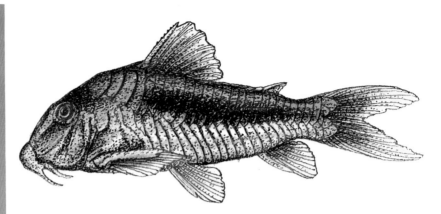

CORYDORAS SOLOX NIJSSEN & ISBRÜCKER, 1983

C. *solox* was described from the Rio Oyapok basin, Amapa territory, Brazil. It reminds one of C. *amapaensis* (also found in the area) but the color patterns differ. C. *solox* does not have the mask and there is no black pigment under the dorsal as in the sympatric species C. *amapaensis*. C. *solox* also has a shorter head and smaller eye than C. *amapaensis*. The care and breeding of this species are the same as that of C. *amapaensis*, although so far there have been no reports of C. *solox* in the hobby.

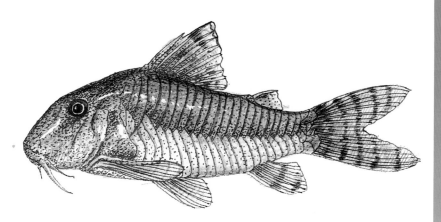

Corydoras spilurus.

CORYDORAS SPILURUS NORMAN, 1926

This is a poorly known species from the Approuage River, French Guiana. It is a long-snouted species resembling *C. octocirrus* but without the third pair of rictal barbels (but does have a triangular skin notch in that same place). It grows to about 5 cm standard length. Aquarium care and breeding are not known but should be identical to other cory species, especially those from the same locality.

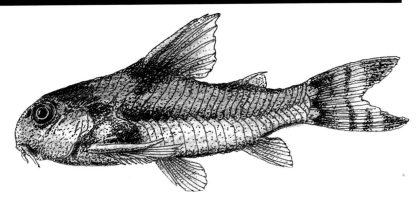

Corydoras steindachneri.

CORYDORAS STEINDACHNERI ISBRÜCKER & NIJSSEN, 1973

This species was described from Parnagua, Estado Parana, southern Brazil, on the basis of only two specimens, both about 4.0 cm in standard length (about 6 cm total length maximum). It is a peaceful but active fish that is best kept in a single species tank or a tank with non-aggressive fishes. Should one be able to get wild-caught animals, it is advised that an acclimatization time be observed and extreme care regarding the water chemistry be taken. Twice weekly water changes are recommended. Aquarium raised animals are much more hardy and less troublesome. A 15- to 20-gallon (or larger) tank should be sufficient for a group. Proper water conditions include a pH of 6.0-7.2, a hardness of up to 15°dGH, and a temperature range of 22-26°C. Food is no problem as most foods are acceptable. For wild-caught individuals living foods should be offered at first, then frozen or dried foods added when the new arrivals are accustomed to their surroundings. *C. steindachneri* spawn normally for the genus. The males are slightly smaller and less rotund and have a longer, more pointed dorsal fin. Apparently this species is related to *C. macropterus* but it does not develop large fins in adults as does *macropterus*. It has two large, round, midlateral brown blotches.

Corydoras stenocephalus. Photo by D. D. Sands.

CORYDORAS STENOCEPHALUS EIGENMANN & ALLEN, 1942

C. stenocephalus was described from "Yarinacocha" (Rio Ucayali system) in Peru. It grows to about 6.5 cm in standard length. This is a long-snouted form that has a diamond or kite shaped blotch on the body extending from the shoulder to about the adipose fin. It is closely related to *C. acutus* but *acutus* has a dorsal blotch and vertical bars in the caudal fin that this species lacks. The proportional and meristic characters are the same. Very few individuals seem to have been imported to the aquarium hobby and no reports on care and breeding are available. It would be best to start them in conditions that are used for other Ucayali species of known habits. No difficulties are expected in keeping this species.

Corydoras sterbai.
Photo by Burkhard Kahl.

CORYDORAS STERBAI KNAACK, 1962

This attractive species comes from the upper Rio Guapore, a border river between Brazil and Bolivia. It is a peaceful and social species that does best in small aggregations. If kept in a community tank it should be housed with species of the middle and upper layers. *C. sterbai* attains a length of about 8 cm and a group can be kept in a tank of about 20- to 25-gallon capacity. The water should be clean, clear, and soft, with some current provided. The pH should be 6.6-7.0, the hardness up to about 12-15°dGH, and the temperature range about 21-25°C. The tank should not be too thickly planted so that more swimming room is available. This species eats all foods, but live foods are preferred. The coloration and pattern remind one of the closely related *C. haraldschultzi.* The essential differences are in the head pattern wherein *C. sterbai* essentially has a dark head with light spots and *C. haraldschultzi* has a pale head with black spotting. Also in *C. sterbai* there is a yellow to weakly orange-colored dorsal spine and brilliant orange-colored pectoral spines. The fins are similar but not so intensively spotted as in *C. haraldschultzi.*

CORYDORAS SURINAMENSIS NIJSSEN, 1970

C. *surinamensis* was discovered in a creek of the Coppename River, Saramacca, Surinam. Nijssen originally described this species as a subspecies of *schwartzi, C. schwartzi surinamensis,* but later raised it to full specific status. It differs from *schwartzi* by having a less deep body, shorter dorsal and pectoral spines, and a smaller eye. Its black blotch ventral to the dorsal fin also covers a larger area of the body. No sex differences are known. This is a peaceful species of about 6 cm that is best kept in groups in a 15- to 20-gallon tank. It is said to be somewhat sensitive to higher nitrate concentrations. Therefore regular water changes of 1/3 to 1/2 every 2-3 weeks are recommended. A pH of 6.0-7.2, a hardness of up to 15°dGH, and a temperature range of 22-25°C are the chemical and physical parameters. Live, frozen, and dried foods are all accepted.

Corydoras cf. *surinamensis.*

Corydoras sychri.
Photo by Dr.
Herbert R. Axelrod.

Corydoras sychri.
Photo by A.
Hogeborn.

CORYDORAS SYCHRI WEITZMAN, 1961

This species was described on the basis of aquarium specimens donated by a Mr. A. Sychr but without specific locality. The type locality was later restricted by Nijssen & Isbrücker to Rio Nanay, Maynas, Loreto, Peru. It attains a size of 5.2 cm. *C. sychri* has a longer snout than its closest relative *C. atropersonatus*. The care and breeding are the same as far as known.

Corydoras treitlii.

CORYDORAS TREITLII STEINDACHNER, 1906

C. treitlii was discovered in influxes to the Rio Parahyba in the vicinity of Pernambuco, Estado Maranhao, eastern Brazil. It is a peaceful, schooling species that needs at least a 20-gallon tank for a group. The temperature range should be 20-25°C. It attains a maximum length of about 7 cm. Unfortunately it is only infrequently available in the tropical fish trade. *C. treitlii* is close to *C. semiaquilus*. Please refer to the writeup of that species for differences.

Corydoras trilineatus. Photo by Burkhard Kahl.

CORYDORAS TRILINEATUS COPE, 1871

C. trilineatus is known from Peru (Rio Ampiyacu in the Departamento Loreto, Rio Morona, forest lake Yarina Cocha, Rio Ucayali system) and Ecuador (Rio Pastaza system). It was incorrectly referred to as C. julii in much of the earlier aquarium literature. Spawning has been accomplished on many occasions, typically as in the following accounts. In a 50 x 35 x 25 cm tank with water at a pH of 6.8, a hardness of 2.5°dGH, a conductivity of 25-40 uS, and a temperature of 28°C, spawning occurred during the months of November to February. The air occasionally was 2-4°C cooler than the tank water. Although 5 males and 3 females were available to spawn, it was always one and the same male that spawned with one or even two spawn-ready females. Two males started to drive the females in the morning hours, but one of the males possibly "turned off" the second male who soon stopped his courting. Mostly only one, rarely two eggs are laid and deposited in the Java moss and once in a great while on the glass panes of the aquarium. On average about 40-60 eggs are laid of which perhaps maximally 35 fry will hatch out, the remaining eggs fungusing. They can be fed with live and frozen rotifers and *Cyclops* nauplii; later chopped tubificid worms and sieved *Daphnia* can be added. With daily water changes to keep pollution levels low they grow quite fast. After about 60 days the black spot in the dorsal makes its appearance. Archner recommends a sex ratio of 2-3:1. His spawnings occurred from December until March. The tank conditions were a pH of 7.0, a hardness of 15°dGH, and a temperature range of 23-25°C. Eventually 30-40 eggs were deposited by one female on broad-leaved water plants. The fry hatched out on about the 4th to 6th day, and feeding with microworms and rotifers was started on the 3rd day after that. Later, newly hatched brine shrimp can be fed. In spite of water changes a high mortality may occur during the first weeks of life. It has been suggested that spawning losses could probably be reduced by feeding microworms.

*Corydoras
triseriatus.*

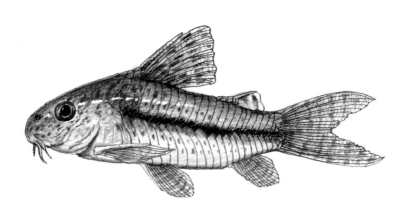

CORYDORAS TRISERIATUS VON IHERING, 1911

This is a doubtful species from southeastern Brazil. It closely resembles *C. nattereri* and in fact may even be synonymous with that species. Those who differ say that *C. triseriatus* is more slender and has a more pointed head. The coloration of the body is lighter, and there is a dark zone before the dorsal fin of *C. nattereri* that is lacking in *triseriatus*. This is a peaceful schooling fish that attains a length of about 8 cm. A 20- to 30-gallon tank should house a nice group. The temperature range should be 22-26°C. Food is no problem as it eats anything. Anything said about *C. nattereri* regarding aquarium care and breeding should apply to this one as well.

CORYDORAS UNDULATUS REGAN, 1912

C. undulatus comes from the La Plata region, Buenos Aires, Argentina. It attains a maximum size of 5.5 cm (4.4 cm standard length). This is not an active detritus feeder and should preferably be given live foods such as *Daphnia*, tubificid worms, mosquito larvae, etc. *C. undulatus* is a distinctive species with regard to its color pattern. Several horizontal dark stripes cross the body which may coalesce to produce an almost completely dark fish with either isolated light spots or longitudinal light lines (the lowermost one the most complete). The head is mottled or vermiculated with dark lines and the dorsal fin sometimes has dark markings. *C. undulatus* is close to *C. nanus* but that species has more light areas. Normal aquarium conditions and spawning techniques can be applied to this species.

Corydoras undulatus. Photo by Burkhard Kahl.

Corydoras weitzmani.

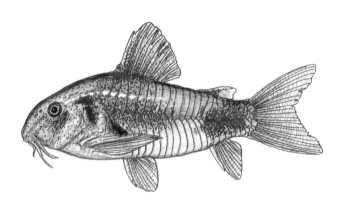

CORYDORAS WEITZMANI NIJSSEN, 1971

Discovered near Cusco, Peru, this species ascends to a higher altitude than any other species of *Corydoras* — 3350 meters above sea level. Being from such an altitude this is one of the cooler water species that does not like warmth. The color pattern is distinctive. It is a pale fish with a dark mask and two large black blotches on the body. The first blotch is on the anterior body and extends up to the anterior part of the dorsal fin; the second blotch covers most of the area between the adipose and anal fins. It attains a length of about 4.7 cm standard length.

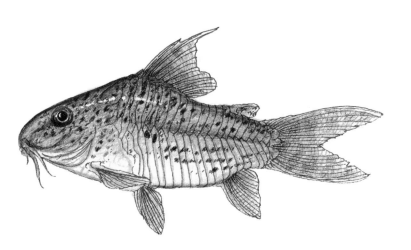

Corydoras xinguensis.

CORYDORAS XINGUENSIS NIJSSEN, 1972

As the name implies, this species is from a tributary of the upper Rio Xingu, Estado Mato Grosso, Brazil. It is most closely related to *C. polystictus* and according to Nijssen may even prove to be a subspecies of that species. *C. polystictus* lacks the pigment on the anterior dorsal fin rays and caudal fin which is present in *C. xinguensis* (in caudal fin as irregular vertical bars). The dark brown spots on the body and head are much larger in *C. xinguensis* than the minute spots of *C. polystictus*. This species attains a standard length of 4.3 cm.

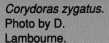
Corydoras zygatus. Photo by D. Lambourne.

CORYDORAS ZYGATUS EIGENMANN & ALLEN, 1942

C. zygatus was collected first in a creek, Yurimaguas, in the Rio Huallaga system, Loreto, Peru. Besides this area of Peru, it is also found in the Rio Pastaza, Ecuador. It is a peaceful, social fish that is constantly searching for food. In the aquarium the favorite foods are tubifex, whiteworms, and chopped earthworms. Flake foods are also taken but they must be soaked so that they drop to the bottom quickly. The water should be slightly acid with a hardness of up to 20°dGH (but 10° is better), and a temperature range of 22-25°C. The 15- to 20-gallon tank should have a dark substrate and a darkened water surface, perhaps by using some floating plants. Peat filtration is also recommended by some aquarists. C. zygatus attains a standard length to 5.6 cm. Females are the larger and fuller animals. Spawning is not difficult to achieve. It may be triggered by a drastic water change of up to 90% and a reduction of the water temperature from 21°C to 17°C or even to 15°C. Once started, spawning follows normal procedures with the T-position assumed. Females deposit some 400-600 eggs on the glass of all four tank sides usually within 2 3/5 inches from the water's surface. Some eggs are even placed above the water line in spawning enthusiasm. The eggs are released in batches of 10-20 into the female's ventral fin basket. Typically, after spawning, adults are removed as a precaution rather than from necessity.

Fry should be fed on the second day after hatching. Microworms supplemented by brine shrimp nauplii alternated with pre-soaked flake foods is suggested. The fry are very differently colored from *C. rabauti*, starting from a spotted pattern through about six weeks (about 18 mm), then changing to a solid dark band from behind the head to the base of the caudal fin. In spite of this the two species are very close. Additional comparisons are given under the writeup of *C. rabauti*.

GENUS
ASPIDORAS

1. *Aspidoras albater* 34

2. *Aspidoras brunneus*

3. *Aspidoras carvalhoi* 36

4. *Aspidoras eurycephalus* 37

5. *Aspidoras fuscoguttatus*

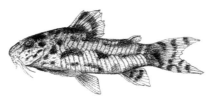

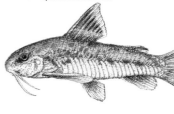

6. *Aspidoras lakoi* 39

7. *Aspidoras maculosus* 40

8. *Aspidoras menezesi*

9. *Aspidoras pauciradiatus* 43

10. *Aspidoras poecilus* 45

11. *Aspidoras raimundi*

12. *Aspidoras rochai* 47

13. *Aspidoras spilotus* 48

14. *Aspidoras virgulatus*

GENUS
BROCHIS

15. *Brochis britskii*   51

16. *Brochis multiradiatus*   55

GENUS
CORYDORAS

17. *Brochis splendens*   57

18. *Corydoras acrensis*   61

19. *Corydoras acutus*   62

20. *Corydoras adolfoi*   63

21. *Corydoras aeneus*   66

22. *Corydoras agassizi*   73

23. *Corydoras amapaensis*   74

24. *Corydoras ambiacus*   75

25. *Corydoras amphibelus*   76

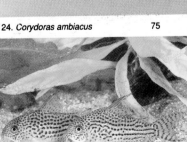

26. *Corydoras approuaguensis*   77

27. *Corydoras araguaiaensis*   78

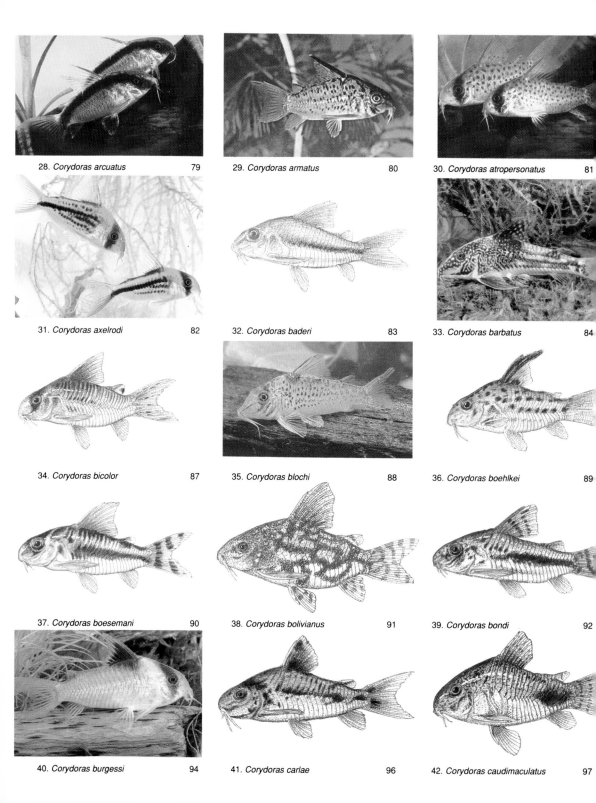

28. *Corydoras arcuatus*   79

29. *Corydoras armatus*   80

30. *Corydoras atropersonatus*   81

31. *Corydoras axelrodi*   82

32. *Corydoras baderi*   83

33. *Corydoras barbatus*   84

34. *Corydoras bicolor*   87

35. *Corydoras blochi*   88

36. *Corydoras boehlkei*   89

37. *Corydoras boesemani*   90

38. *Corydoras bolivianus*   91

39. *Corydoras bondi*   92

40. *Corydoras burgessi*   94

41. *Corydoras carlae*   96

42. *Corydoras caudimaculatus*   97

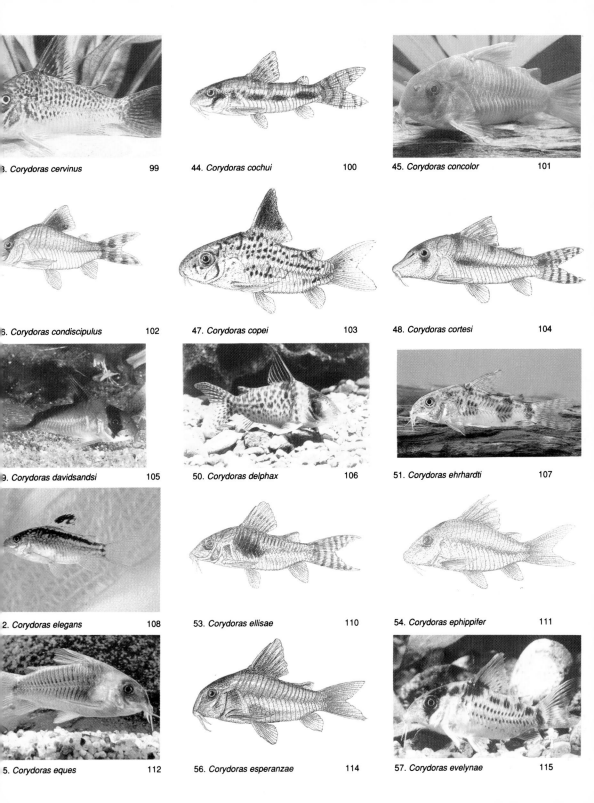

43. *Corydoras cervinus* 99

44. *Corydoras cochui* 100

45. *Corydoras concolor* 101

46. *Corydoras condiscipulus* 102

47. *Corydoras copei* 103

48. *Corydoras cortesi* 104

49. *Corydoras davidsandsi* 105

50. *Corydoras delphax* 106

51. *Corydoras ehrhardti* 107

52. *Corydoras elegans* 108

53. *Corydoras ellisae* 110

54. *Corydoras ephippifer* 111

55. *Corydoras eques* 112

56. *Corydoras esperanzae* 114

57. *Corydoras evelynae* 115

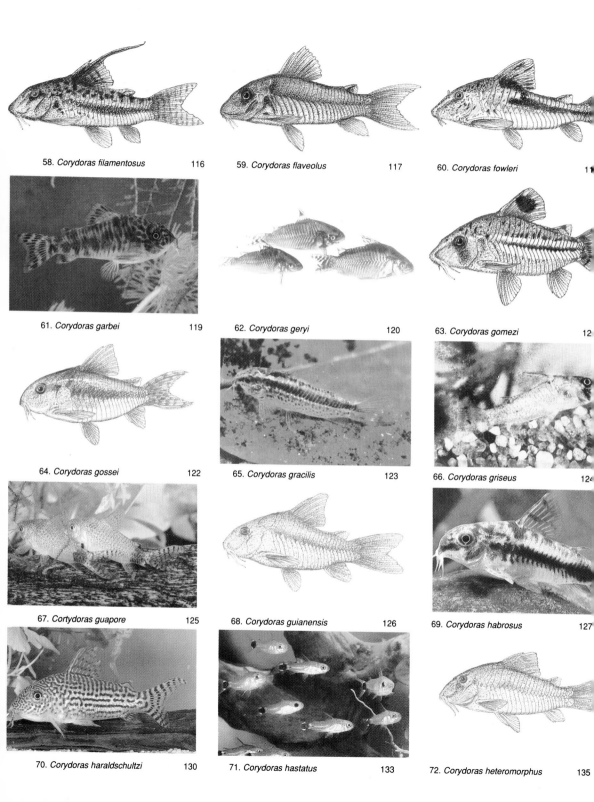

58. *Corydoras filamentosus* 116

59. *Corydoras flaveolus* 117

60. *Corydoras fowleri* 11

61. *Corydoras garbei* 119

62. *Corydoras geryi* 120

63. *Corydoras gomezi* 12

64. *Corydoras gossei* 122

65. *Corydoras gracilis* 123

66. *Corydoras griseus* 124

67. *Cortydoras guapore* 125

68. *Corydoras guianensis* 126

69. *Corydoras habrosus* 127

70. *Corydoras haraldschultzi* 130

71. *Corydoras hastatus* 133

72. *Corydoras heteromorphus* 135

73. *Corydoras imitator*   136

74. *Corydoras julii*   137

75. *Corydoras lamberti*   138

76. *Corydoras latus*   139

77. *Corydoras leopardus*   140

78. *Corydoras leucomelas*   142

79. *Corydoras loretoensis*   143

80. *Corydoras loxozonus*   144

81. *Cortydoras macropterus*   145

82. *Corydoras maculifer*   147

83. *Corydoras melanistius brevirostris*   148

84. *Corydoras melanistius melanistius* 149

85. *Corydoras melanotaenia*   150

86. *Corydoras melini*   151

87. *Corydoras metae*   152

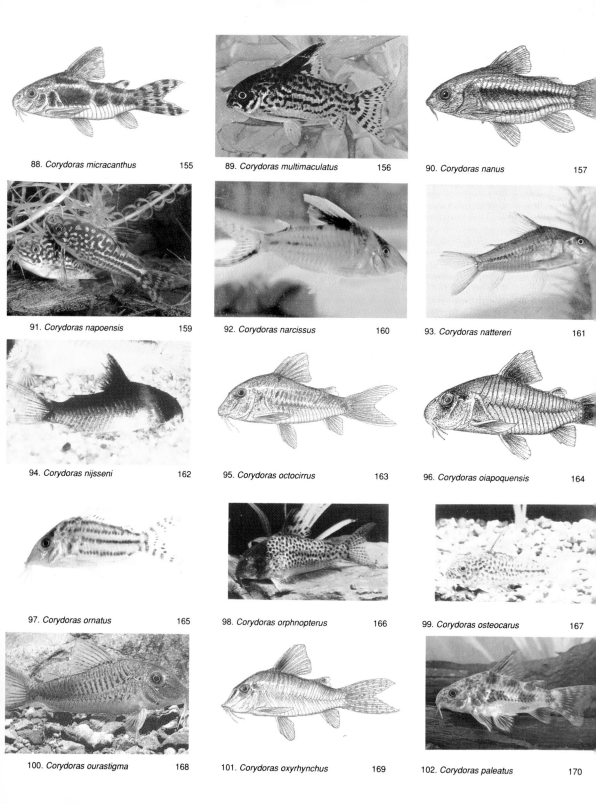

88. *Corydoras micracanthus*   155

89. *Corydoras multimaculatus*   156

90. *Corydoras nanus*   157

91. *Corydoras napoensis*   159

92. *Corydoras narcissus*   160

93. *Corydoras nattereri*   161

94. *Corydoras nijsseni*   162

95. *Corydoras octocirrus*   163

96. *Corydoras oiapoquensis*   164

97. *Corydoras ornatus*   165

98. *Corydoras orphnopterus*   166

99. *Corydoras osteocarus*   167

100. *Corydoras ourastigma*   168

101. *Corydoras oxyrhynchus*   169

102. *Corydoras paleatus*   170

103. *Corydoras panda*   172

104. *Corydoras pastazensis*   175

105. *Corydoras polystictus*   176

106. *Corydoras potaroensis*   178

107. *Corydoras prionotus*   179

108. *Corydoras pulcher*   180

109. *Corydoras pygmaeus*   181

110. *Corydoras rabauti*   184

111. *Corydoras reticulatus*   188

112. *Corydoras reynoldsi*   189

113. *Corydoras robinae*   190

114. *Corydoras robustus*   191

115. *Corydoras sanchesi*   192

116. *Corydoras saramaccensis*   193

117. *Corydoras schwartzi*   194

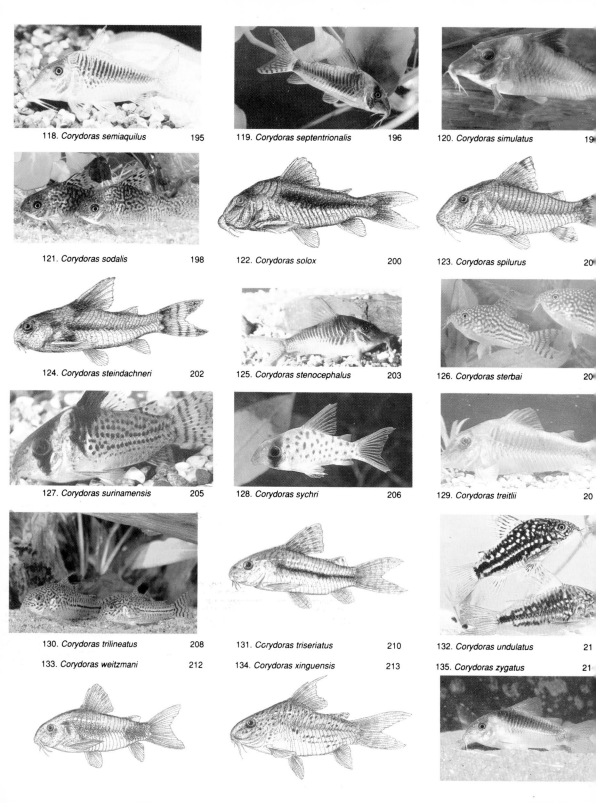

118. *Corydoras semiaquilus*   195

119. *Corydoras septentrionalis*   196

120. *Corydoras simulatus*   19

121. *Corydoras sodalis*   198

122. *Corydoras solox*   200

123. *Corydoras spilurus*   20

124. *Corydoras steindachneri*   202

125. *Corydoras stenocephalus*   203

126. *Corydoras sterbai*   20

127. *Corydoras surinamensis*   205

128. *Corydoras sychri*   206

129. *Corydoras treitlii*   20

130. *Corydoras trilineatus*   208

131. *Ccrydoras triseriatus*   210

132. *Corydoras undulatus*   21

133. *Corydoras weitzmani*   212

134. *Corydoras xinguensis*   213

135. *Corydoras zygatus*   21